INDIANS

Pocahontas, *Seymour*
Sacagawea, *Seymour*
Sequoyah, *Snow*
Sitting Bull, *Stevenson*
Squanto, *Stevenson*
Tecumseh, *Stevenson*

NAVAL HEROES

David Farragut, *Long*
George Dewey, *Long*
John Paul Jones, *Snow*
Matthew Calbraith Perry, *Scharbach*
Oliver Hazard Perry, *Long*
Raphael Semmes, *Snow*
Stephen Decatur, *Smith*

NOTED WIVES and MOTHERS

Abigail Adams, *Wagoner*
Dolly Madison, *Monsell*
Jessie Fremont, *Wagoner*
Martha Washington, *Wagoner*
Mary Todd Lincoln, *Wilkie*
Nancy Hanks, *Stevenson*
Rachel Jackson, *Govan*

SCIENTISTS and INVENTORS

Albert Einstein, *Hammontree*
Aleck Bell, *Widdemer*
Cyrus McCormick, *Dobler*
Eli Whitney, *Snow*
Elias Howe, *Corcoran*
Elizabeth Blackwell, *Henry*
George Carver, *Stevenson*
George Eastman, *Henry*
Henry Ford, *Aird and Ruddiman*
John Audubon, *Mason*
Luther Burbank, *Burt*
Maria Mitchell, *Melin*
Robert Fulton, *Henry*
Samuel Morse, *Snow*
Tom Edison, *Guthridge*
Walter Reed, *Higgins*
Wilbur and Orville Wright, *Stevenson*
Will and Charlie Mayo, *Hammontree*

SOCIAL and CIVIC LEADERS

Jane Add
J. Sterling Morton,
Julia Ward Howe, *Wagoner*
Juliette Low, *Higgins*
Liliuokalani, *Newman*
Lucretia Mott, *Burnett*
Molly Pitcher, *Stevenson*
Oliver Wendell Holmes, Jr., *Dunham*
Susan Anthony, *Monsell*

SOLDIERS

Anthony Wayne, *Stevenson*
Bedford Forrest, *Parks*
Dan Morgan, *Bryant*
Ethan Allen, *Winders*
Francis Marion, *Steele*
Israel Putnam, *Stevenson*
Jeb Stuart, *Winders*
Nathanael Greene, *Peckham*
Robert E. Lee, *Monsell*
Sam Houston, *Stevenson*
Tom Jackson, *Monsell*
U. S. Grant, *Stevenson*
William Henry Harrison, *Peckham*
Zack Taylor, *Wilkie*

STATESMEN

Abe Lincoln, *Stevenson*
Andy Jackson, *Stevenson*
Dan Webster, *Smith*
Franklin Roosevelt, *Weil*
Henry Clay, *Monsell*
James Monroe, *Widdemer*
Jeff Davis, *de Grummond and Delaune*
John Marshall, *Monsell*
Teddy Roosevelt, *Parks*
Woodrow Wilson, *Monsell*

Rachel Jackson

Tennessee Girl

Illustrated by Robert Doremus

Rachel Jackson

Tennessee Girl

By Christine Noble Govan

THE BOBBS-MERRILL COMPANY, INC.
A SUBSIDIARY OF HOWARD W. SAMS & CO., INC.
Publishers • INDIANAPOLIS • NEW YORK

LIBRARY OF CONGRESS CATALOG CARD NUMBER: 62-16607

PRINTED IN THE UNITED STATES OF AMERICA

To Mary and William Steele,
with love and with appreciation
of their own fine work.

Illustrations

Full pages

Contents

★ ★

Books by Christine Noble Govan

RACHEL JACKSON: TENNESSEE GIRL

★ # Rachel Jackson

Tennessee Girl

Girls' Work or Boys' Fun

A BIG log house stood in the forest near the Banister River of southern Virginia. It belonged to Mr. John Donelson. The March day was warm, and Mrs. Donelson had left the cabin door open. She stood tying the strings of her bonnet under her chin. Her youngest daughter Rachel sat on a stool by the hearth and watched her mother.

"Is Mrs. Simpson's baby very new?" Rachel asked. "Did she just get it?"

Mrs. Donelson smiled. "Very new. Just one day old." She picked up her shawl and placed it around her shoulders.

"Then how can he eat chicken soup?" Rachel went on. "Leven didn't have any teeth. Does this baby have teeth?"

"I'm taking the soup to Mrs. Simpson."

"Why doesn't Mrs. Simpson make her own soup? Doesn't she have plenty of fat hens?"

"No, the Simpsons are very poor, and they're a large family. I'm afraid Mrs. Simpson may not have the nourishing food she needs."

Rachel felt very sorry for their neighbor. "Then I'm glad Candis made such a big kettle of soup. Please take it all to Mrs. Simpson."

"I'll stay for a while and visit with her," Mrs. Donelson continued. "Perhaps I can help her with the work, or send one of the servants over later. Is Somerset ready?"

Through the open door Rachel could see the Negro servant. "Yes, he has two horses saddled." Somerset would ride with Mrs. Donelson to protect her from any wild animals or Indians.

Rachel sighed as her mother picked up a square piece of linen. It was a sampler, with a simple design of flowers. Across the bottom the alphabet was worked in red, the numbers 1 to 20 in blue. Below them were the words, "Rachel Donelson, 6 years old, March 1773."

Mrs. Donelson spread the sampler over Rachel's lap. "Dear, you have two more flowers to work. And all the stitches in your name are crooked. While I'm gone I want you to finish the flowers. Tomorrow I'll help you take out the crooked stitches and you can do your name again. Wouldn't you like to finish this before your father comes home?"

"Oh, yes, Mother, but he won't be here until next week. I want to go with Sam today! We're going to—"

"Rachel, yesterday you spent hours looking for duck eggs with Sam. The day before that, you fell into the creek with Sam."

"Today Sam and I are going to be out with the colts," Rachel explained.

"Today your brother will have to play alone," Mrs. Donelson declared. "Young ladies who play with colts and chase rabbits through the woods don't finish their tasks."

"Mother, I don't chase rabbits! I just go along with Sam through the woods. The dogs chase the rabbits."

In spite of her stern look, Mrs. Donelson's eyes twinkled. She was quite sure that Rachel would learn housekeeping skills before long.

"Well, Rachel," she said, "I don't intend to teach our dogs how to behave. It takes all my time to train my daughters—Mary, Catherine, Jane and now you. I'll expect you to have the flowers done when I return."

She stepped out the door. "Jane!" she called. "Please come here. Let me talk with you for a moment before I go to see Mrs. Simpson."

Rachel's older sister came from the small log cabin, a few feet away, where the food was prepared. Mrs. Donelson gave Jane some directions about supper.

Rachel sighed and picked up the needle and thread. She began to work on her sampler. Presently she heard the sound of horses' hoofs. Her mother and Somerset were trotting away between the trees.

Jane came into the house, followed by two of her brothers. Sam was a year older than Rachel, and Severn was four years older.

"Come on, Rachel," Sam urged. "Peter is going to break the new colt. Don't you want to watch him?"

"For shame!" Jane said sharply. She was nearly twenty and when she spoke the younger children listened. "Here's Rachel sewing as Mother told her to, and you rascals try to tempt her away!"

Jane picked up a turkey wing and swept the ashes off the hearth. "And don't bother a groom who is training a colt," she went on. "I saw you yesterday when Peter was shoeing the brown mare. The poor man hardly had room to turn with you boys crowding around him. Now mind what I say and keep out of the way!"

Jane put away the turkey-wing brush and returned to the kitchen to help Candis, the cook.

"Wheee!" Severn exclaimed. "I'm glad I'm not a girl. I'd hate to sit by the fire and sew."

"Me too," Sam added—but not very loudly. He was fond of his pretty little sister. The boys had more fun when Rachel was with them. She always thought of new things to do.

Rachel stitched away. She knew they were only teasing. Every girl must learn to sew. She was proud when her stitches were small and even. Still, it was hard to stay inside when everything outdoors was green and fresh.

"Girls are just as good as boys," she said finally. "They can do things as well as boys can when they have the chance."

"They can't fight so well," Severn declared.

Rachel didn't answer. Suddenly she sprang up from her stool. She flung the sampler over Severn's face and grabbed at his legs. In his surprise he lost his balance and fell.

"Girls can fight just as well as boys," Rachel announced. She sat down primly again.

Sam shouted with laughter.

Severn pulled the sampler from his face. He still looked surprised. "I guess they can," he admitted. "At least you can."

"Rachel really fixed you." Sam chuckled. "A little-bitty girl knocking down a boy ten years old! Wait till Rachel is ten!"

Severn laughed and rubbed his knees. "If the Indians come around this spring, we'll just let Rachel fight them," he said as they went out.

For a while the little girl sewed steadily, while the fire crackled. She wondered what the boys were doing. She wished she could watch Peter. The new colt was so pretty! Father had said perhaps she might have a pony of her own next year.

She wished someone would come in and talk to her. But no one was near the house. Her older brothers, John, William and Stockley, were helping the field hands cut down forest trees and underbrush, to make a new field. Jane would be busy in the kitchen for another hour.

Rachel wished her baby brother, Leven, were at home. He was so funny he was always good company. But sister Catherine, who was married and had a home of her own, had "borrowed" him for a week.

Father was even farther away. He helped to make the laws for the Colony of Virginia. Now he was in the town of Williamsburg, the capital, where the House of Burgesses was meeting.

Suddenly Rachel heard the dogs' loud, excited barks in the distance. She dropped her sewing and ran to the door. Everything looked just as it always did. There were the kitchen and the smokehouse, then the stables and barn, and past them the cabins where the servants lived. Beyond the cabins were the cornfields. Beyond the fields was the dense, silent forest where Rachel and her brothers loved to play.

What a racket the dogs were making! Had Indians come out of the woods? For a minute Rachel felt cold with fear. Then around the corner of the kitchen hopped a tiny rabbit. It paused by the house. Rachel could see its big frightened eyes. Its pink ears twitched.

The dogs were after the poor baby rabbit! She knew it couldn't go much farther.

Rachel hated to see any animal hurt. And this was such a darling little rabbit! Now it moved in big leaps across the yard to the woods.

The Donelson's two big hounds, Nellie and Old Tom, raced about the outside of the kitchen log cabin, yelling wildly. In a flash Rachel ran from the house.

"Nellie," she screamed, "stop! Come back, Old Tom! Come here!"

Rachel was across the yard and into the woods in no time. As she ran she called the dogs, but they paid no attention to her. By this time she was hot and breathless. Brambles caught at her long dress and tore it. Branches slashed her face. She stumbled and fell. When she got to her feet, mud streaked the front of her dress. Her face and arms were scratched.

The dogs were in a blackberry thicket at the edge of the clearing. Their yelps faded away to whimpers. Rachel knew the rabbit must have escaped in the tangle of vines. She sat down on the mossy grass to catch her breath. "I'm glad the rabbit got away," she thought.

Then she heard a clucking sound near her. On her hands and knees she crept in its direction. Had one of their hens made a nest out here? Rachel pushed aside some branches and saw a wild turkey hen pecking at the ground. It was feeding on seeds.

She watched it for a while. "I guess her nest is close by," Rachel decided. "Maybe I can find it before the boys do."

She crawled through the long grass. She looked under bushes and behind stumps. Finally, against a fallen tree where the grass grew tall, she found the nest. There were twelve eggs in it.

"I wonder if I could raise a turkey," Rachel said to herself. "I'm sure Aunt Callie would let me put the eggs under the setting hen."

Aunt Callie was an old woman who worked for the Donelsons. She was Somerset's mother and a great favorite with Rachel.

Carefully the little girl slipped three eggs from the nest. On the way back she met Sam and Severn, who were going to see the colt.

"What are you carrying?" Severn asked.

"Wild turkey eggs," she answered, and hurried on. She wanted to get them under the hen before they grew cold.

"Turkey eggs!" Sam echoed. "Let's make a fire and roast them."

"Good gracious, no!" cried Rachel, shocked. "I want to raise some turkeys."

"Wild turkey eggs won't hatch," Severn said.

"Maybe mine will," Rachel said hopefully.

Sam laughed. "You'd better wash that mud off your face and get back to your sewing. What will Mother say when she sees you?"

Rachel stopped still. She had forgotten all about her sampler! For a moment she stood with the eggs in her hands, not knowing what to do. "It isn't far to Aunt Callie's," she said at last. "I'll hurry right back."

Holding the eggs carefully, she ran to the cabin where Aunt Callie lived. She knocked on the battered door.

"Come in," called an old, high voice.

Rachel opened the door and went in. Quickly she told Aunt Callie what she wanted to do.

"Why, sure now, honey child!" Aunt Callie agreed. "We'll raise those turkeys. I'll just slip the eggs under my old hen. It will be no trouble."

Rachel looked into the wrinkled face and smiled. "Thank you, Aunt Callie. I know we can raise some turkeys. They will be my very own because I found them, but I'll give one to you because you're helping me."

"The eggs will surely hatch," Aunt Callie promised. "I'll take care of them."

"I have to go now," Rachel explained. "I have to finish my sewing. But I'll come back early tomorrow and see about our eggs."

A few minutes later Rachel sat again by the hearth. She had not stopped to wash her hands. Some of the mud and grass stains on them rubbed off on the sampler. But by the time Mrs. Donelson returned, the flowers were nearly finished.

When she came in, Rachel sprang up. "See, Mother! And almost all the stitches are straight."

Mrs. Donelson smiled at her little daughter. Then she glanced down at the sampler and noticed the dirt on the embroidery. She saw Rachel's grimy hands and face. Her smile faded.

"Rachel, how did you get your hands so dirty? And look at your dress! Have you been outdoors?" Her voice was gentle, but it sounded unhappy too.

"Yes, Mother," Rachel answered in a low tone.

"Oh, Rachel, after I had forbidden it! I'm sorry, my dear, but you will have to go to bed without supper and without hearing Jane read aloud to us."

Big tears rolled down Rachel's cheeks. It was bad enough to miss supper. But how could she bear to miss the fun after supper? She loved to sit with all her brothers in front of the fire while her mother sewed and Jane read from the Bible, or from some book of stories.

"Oh, I wish I'd never seen the rabbit!"

Mrs. Donelson looked more unhappy. "Oh, Rachel, you were out chasing rabbits instead of doing your sewing? Apparently you pay no attention to what I tell you."

"But, Mother, it was such a tiny rabbit—and Nellie and Old Tan were so big, and they were after it. I couldn't bear to see it killed. I just wanted to help it get away."

Mrs. Donelson listened gravely to the story. Then she said, "I understand, Rachel. I know you thought only of protecting a helpless little animal. And I am glad that you have a kind heart. So I won't punish you, even though you disobeyed me."

She picked up the sampler and looked at it closely. "You sew faster than I thought you could. You've done not only the work I told you to do, but have also found time to go rabbit chasing. However, there's room for another row of flowers underneath this row."

Rachel looked at it without enthusiasm. She had hoped it was nearly finished.

"Tomorrow you'll stay indoors and add those and your name," Mrs. Donelson went on. "Then you will have a really fine sampler to show your father when he comes home."

Rachel smiled through her tears. "All right, Mother," she answered sweetly. "I'll promise not to go out tomorrow till the sampler is finished. If the dogs run by chasing anything, I—I'll just look the other way!"

Rachel's Guests

THE NEXT week there were great preparations for Mr. Donelson's home-coming. The house was cleaned. The silver and pewter were polished. The boys caught chickens to cook for pies. They had to chase the cackling hens all around the barnyard.

Rachel hurried out to join the chase.

Jane called after her, "You mustn't go in the barnyard! It's too muddy."

"But I want to help the boys," Rachel cried.

"No indeed," Jane said firmly. "The boys will track in enough mud! You run down and get Aunt Callie right away."

"What do you want her for?" asked Rachel.

"Mother wants her to make the pastry for the pies," Jane explained. "No one else has such a light hand with it."

Rachel felt happy as she skipped toward Aunt Callie's cabin. She was glad to be outdoors, but she hadn't really wanted to chase chickens."

When she knocked, Aunt Callie hobbled to the door. The old woman was crippled with rheumatism and today could not get about very easily.

"Aunt Callie, Mother wants you please to come and make pies for Father. Have my eggs hatched yet?" Rachel added in the same breath.

"Child, I ain't had time to look at the old hen today. Let's go out and look right now."

Aunt Callie put on a clean turban. Then she and Rachel walked around behind the cabin to a little coop. There the brooding hen sat on her nest. Eagerly Rachel peered in. The hen clucked anxiously.

"Now let me see." Aunt Callie stooped to put her hand in the nest. A little head popped out from under the hen's wing.

"Look—a baby turkey!" Rachel said in delight. "I've never seen one before."

"It sure is," Aunt Callie answered. "We'll leave the old hen alone. She'll take care of your turkey. Soon you'll have a big old gobbler, honey. He'll grow fast."

When she came back to the house, Rachel begged to ride with Severn and Sam to meet their father. She was eager to see him.

"No," Mrs. Donelson answered, "I think he would rather you waited here. The boys will ride quite a distance, and it's lonely on the trail. Somerset will have enough to do, keeping an eye on Severn and Sam. He will be too busy to look after you also."

Rachel turned away sadly. She could not persuade Mother to change her mind.

"Besides," Mrs. Donelson said, "there are still tasks to finish before Father comes. We need your help, Rachel." The little girl felt more cheerful. She liked to feel that she was big enough to be useful.

It seemed hours before the boys rode back with Mr. Donelson. When all the pewter was polished, Rachel began to watch for them. She ran from window to door, peering down the trail. Wouldn't they ever come?

At last she heard the sound of hoofbeats. Sam galloped up to the house first. He slid from his horse and ran to Rachel. He shouted, "Father has brought presents—something for each of us!"

Rachel danced in excitement. Her big dark eyes sparkled and her cheeks were pink. Her dark curls bobbed around her pretty face.

"What is Father bringing me?" she wondered. "Perhaps a doll. Or a barley sugar. Oh, I do wish they'd hurry!"

Father, Severn, and Somerset did not gallop. They rode slowly into the clearing and then to the stables. Rachel wondered why they didn't hurry. Didn't Father care about seeing his children? Hadn't he missed his family?

Why did Father have to talk so long to Somerset? Why didn't he come inside?

Mr. Donelson dismounted and turned toward the house. Rachel wanted to run to meet him, but she remembered what Jane had said about the mud and stayed where she was. She wanted to look nice for Father.

At the door he called back to Somerset, "When King gets here with the rest of the horses and the baggage, tell him to come to the house."

Rachel was terribly disappointed. Had Father left the presents far down the trail? How could she possibly wait longer?

"Father," she cried as he stepped in, "what did you bring me?"

He laughed and caught Rachel up in his arms. He swung her high in the air. "That's a fine welcome!" he teased. "Do you care more for a present than you do for me?"

"No, no!" Rachel hugged him. She loved her handsome father dearly. Even though he looked very dignified most of the time, he liked to play with his youngest daughter.

Now he set her down and kissed his wife and Jane. William, John and Stockley, the oldest brother, came hurrying in from the fields to welcome their father. The house rang with the sound of happy voices. Rachel grew more and more excited. How wonderful it was to have Father at home! How she had missed him!

"Bring me my saddlebags, Severn," he said at last. "They're in the hall by the table."

"Oooh," Rachel breathed. He had brought the presents with him, after all! What would there be for her?

Mr. Donelson handed round the presents. For Jane there was a string of china beads. Fine new hunting knives were given to the younger boys. For William, who liked to read, there was a book. For little Leven there was a wooden ball. Mrs. Donelson smiled when her husband gave her a warm blue shawl. Stockley received a new knife, too, that seemed to please him very much.

But what was there for Rachel? Her eyes grew big. Surely Father had not forgotten her.

Then he drew something else from the bag. A handful of beautiful blue ribbons! And what was that shining among the ribbons? A locket! A tiny gold locket to wear around her neck.

"Oh, Father! Oh, Father!" She reached up and kissed him. She had never owned anything so lovely. She was so excited that she didn't know how to thank him.

"For a pretty little girl—to make her prettier than ever. Let's see how you look."

"I have something for you, too." Rachel ran to a chest to get her sampler. All the stitches were straight and neat. How glad she was she had worked hard on it! Now she had something to give Father in return for his beautiful present.

Her mother said, "John, you spoil the child. I'm afraid she's a little vain now, and you'll make her worse than ever."

"Nonsense, my dear!" Mr. Donelson smiled at his wife. "I'm home so little that my teasing won't do much harm. She's the most kindhearted little body in the world. I'm sure she is not really vain. She just likes to look nice."

A week later the Donelsons had company. A friend of Mr. Donelson came to spend a few days and talk business. His name was Carter. He brought his two daughters, Susan and Nancy. Susan was a year older than Rachel, Nancy a few months younger. The two fathers thought the little girls would enjoy visiting together.

At first Rachel did enjoy her guests. She did not often have a chance to play with girls her own age. She took her visitors around the clearing. She showed them the barn and the stables. She showed them the new colt in the barnyard.

"Next year I'm going to have a pony," she boasted. "Father has practically promised. I hope it runs like the wind."

"I have a kitten all my own," Susan said. "And Nancy has a green bird in a cage."

Rachel was surprised. She had been so busy pointing out all the things on the Donelson place that she had quite forgotten Nancy and Susan might have chickens and stables.

"How nice!" she said. "I have a pet, too. Come on, I'll show you."

The three little girls skipped past the barnyard and around behind Aunt Callie's cabin. A hen clucked to her chicks under a big tree. One long-necked young turkey scratched amid the chicks.

"See." Rachel pointed. "Isn't he wonderful! Aunt Callie and I hatched him from a wild turkey's egg. I had three eggs, but only this one hatched. Aunt Callie says he will be a gobbler when he grows up."

"He's awful ugly." Susan turned away.

"He won't be when he's older," Rachel explained. "Aunt Callie says little turkeys are always ugly."

"I don't like turkeys," Nancy said. "Let's go back inside and play dolls."

For a while they played quietly by the hearth. Rachel soon tired of this. She liked to play dolls, but she wanted her doll to lead an active, exciting life. She wanted her to have an Indian fight or to gallop down the trail. The little Carter girls liked to put their dolls to bed with a fever. Then they would nurse them until they got well.

"Let's take our dolls out under the trees behind the barn," Rachel suggested.

"Bears live in those woods," said Susan. "I heard your father say so. If we went out there, a bear might get us."

Rachel was disgusted. "Well, I'm not afraid. I'm going, and you two can come along or not just as you please. I'm tired of doing the same old thing." She seized her doll and got up.

She started out, but Mrs. Donelson stopped her. "Why, Rachel, you're not leaving your little visitors, are you?"

"But, Mother, they don't want to play any games that are fun!"

"Susan and Nancy are your guests," her mother said firmly. "You must stay and entertain them, no matter what games they want to play."

Rachel went back to the hearth. Nancy and Susan gave her such sad looks that she burst out laughing. "Oh, well," she exclaimed, "I'll let my doll have a fever, if you will doctor and nurse her. At least that will be a change."

For the rest of the visit the little girls got along very well together. The time came for the Carters to leave. Rachel had on her very best dress. She was wearing in her hair the blue ribbons her father had brought her. The new locket hung around her throat.

"Come outside," she called to Nancy and Susan. "I know what we can do."

From the house Mr. and Mrs. Donelson watched the three little girls. "Rachel outshines the Carter children," her father said proudly. "She is so pretty and sturdy."

"Hush, John, Mr. Carter will hear you," Mrs. Donelson answered softly. But she knew it was true. Nancy and Susan were pale, thin children. Their hair was dull and they wore it braided close to their heads. Rachel's dark curls shone and her big brown eyes sparkled. She was strong and lively. Her healthy ways made the other little girls seem paler and plainer than ever.

Nancy, Susan and Rachel walked to a big tree full of fluffy white blossoms. Rachel said it was a serviceberry tree. Its branches grew out over the pen where the pigs were kept.

Rachel climbed up on the rail fence. "Come on up," she urged. "It's just like sitting in a big bouquet up here in the branches."

The Carter girls refused. "I'm wearing my best dress," Nancy answered.

"Ladies shouldn't climb fences." Susan tossed her head. "Only tomboys climb fences. You'd better learn to be a lady."

" 'Fraidy-cats!" Rachel cried. She stood up on the fence to show she wasn't afraid. She let go the branch she was holding and took a step. She held her arms out straight and took another step.

Then . . . she stumbled and fell! Rachel screamed as she landed in the mud. A large pig rose from another puddle near by. It moved toward her, grunting curiously.

Rachel slid and slipped in the mud as she tried to stand. Finally she managed to get to her feet just before the pig reached her. She climbed the fence and wiped the mud from her face.

Susan and Nancy had fled to the house. Rachel followed, sobbing loudly. She was covered with black mud from head to foot.

As Mrs. Donelson bathed her, Rachel told what had happened.

"I wanted to show Nancy and Susan I wasn't afraid of anything," she explained.

"Oh, Rachel!" said Mrs. Donelson sadly. "You've fallen into the pigpen and ruined your best dress, just because you were showing off. 'Pride goeth before a fall.' And how could you be so rude to your guests?"

Rachel looked up in surprise. "Oh, Mother, I didn't mean to be rude!" She began to cry. "I'll—I'll give my blue ribbons to Susan and Nancy. Then I'll remember never to be proud again as long as I live."

Mrs. Donelson knew how much Rachel loved pretty things, and what a sacrifice this would be. "Yes, it may help you learn this lesson."

The ribbons were washed and pressed. Rachel apologized to Susan and Nancy and kissed them. She gave them the ribbons and helped Susan tie hers in her hair. As the Carters rode away, Rachel waved gaily to them.

Later she said to her mother, "I didn't know being proud could make me mean. I'm sorry now. But do you know, I still think I'm just a little bit braver than Susan and Nancy."

Indian Fight

RACHEL hurried toward the house, with her hands cupped around something. Samuel sat in the doorway, whittling.

"Look, Sam! The first ripe persimmons! I found them under the trees at the edge of the woods, hundreds of them."

"Yum-yum!" Sam cried. He took two of the small, wrinkled, orange fruit from her hands. He put one in his mouth. It was sweet and delicious. He ate a second one.

"I thought they'd be ripe soon," he said. "There was frost on the grass this morning—and look! Other things are ripe, too."

Rachel looked to where he pointed. A fat squirrel scurried up a tree. It held a hickory nut in its mouth.

"They have been gathering nuts all morning." Sam tossed an acorn at the squirrel, which ran out on a branch. It sat there, holding the nut in its paws, chattering.

"Aunt Callie says it will be a cold winter." Rachel popped a persimmon into her mouth.

"How can she tell?"

"The moss gets thick on the trees, and the nuts grow plentiful. Aunt Callie says those are both signs of a cold winter."

"Let's take a pail and pick up more persimmons," Sam said. "Maybe Mother will have Candis make a persimmon pudding for supper."

As the two children went toward the kitchen Rachel said, "Last night I heard the wild geese flying south."

"Honk! Honk! Honk!" Sam cried.

Rachel frowned. It wasn't a very good imitation of the wild geese. "No," she said, "they make a sad sound."

Sam nodded. "And that means fall has really come. It's already harvesting time."

This was the fall of the year 1774. Rachel's turkey was now a large gobbler. His tail and wings were beautiful. He was so proud of them that he spread them and strutted whenever anyone came near. The boys teased Rachel by talking about how good Old Gobbler would taste.

"We'll chop his head off," Sam often said, "and eat him the next time Father comes home."

"No! No!" Rachel would protest. "We must never eat him. He's my pet."

Early one morning Rachel and Jane sat at the table, eating porridge. Mrs. Donelson was feeding Leven. Sam was the only one who had finished breakfast. The older boys were still in the loft, where they slept.

"Old Gobbler is so quiet this morning," Rachel remarked. "He hasn't made a sound." She left the table and ran to the window. "And he's walking all crouched over. Oh, Mother, do you think he's sick?"

Mrs. Donelson realized then that the chickens also were unusually quiet. She got up and joined Rachel at the window. Old Gobbler was behaving very strangely. He ran from one side of the yard to the other. He dragged his wings and never raised his head. He seemed afraid.

Mrs. Donelson put little Leven back in his trundle bed, which was pulled out at night from under his parents' large bed. She picked up her shawl and went to the door. "You stay here, Rachel, while I look about. Perhaps a snake or a possum has killed a chicken."

As she stepped outside Mrs. Donelson glanced up. There were no hawks in the sky. There were no wild creatures in the yard.

But Old Gobbler and the chickens were too quiet. Mrs. Donelson felt uneasy. Only one thing could make the fowls so nervous. Some unfamiliar creatures were near by. The fowls were used to forest animals, but they would be disturbed if human strangers approached. It was not hard to guess that Indians were about.

They had not bothered the Donelsons for several years. But there was always danger. Small bands of Indians roamed through the frontier country. They would creep up on lonely farms, steal horses or supplies, and vanish into the forest. If they outnumbered white settlers, sometimes they attacked or burned the cabins.

Mrs. Donelson knew she must not show her children she was afraid. If only her husband had not returned to Williamsburg! If only Stockley had not gone to visit his sister Catherine! The mother and the younger boys would have to protect the house.

She tried to look calm as she opened the door. John, William and Severn had not come down yet. Sam sat by the hearth, mending a thong of his moccasins.

"Sam," his mother said in a low tone, "run up and wake your brothers. Tell them I think Indians are coming. I'll tell the girls. Don't call out," she warned, as Sam sprang up. "Speak very quietly. They may be close to the house. But hurry!"

Sam dashed across the room in his stocking feet. He sped up the ladder like a squirrel. He called softly to his brothers, "Indians! Mother says hurry!"

The boys were already awake and almost dressed. They tumbled down the ladder after Sam. They found Rachel barring the inside shutters at the windows. Jane was laying the guns on the table. They were always kept oiled and ready in the house.

Mrs. Donelson, who had already called Candis to come from the kitchen, now barred the door.

"Oh, Mother, Aunt Callie is alone in her cabin," Rachel cried. "I must go down and warn her right away."

"No!" said William. "If you go out now they may kill you."

Mrs. Donelson caught the little girl as she ran toward the door. "No Rachel," she said quietly, though her face was pale and worried. "There is not time to warn the servants. We'll have to pray that the Lord will protect them. Remember how old and wise Aunt Callie is. She will surely guess why Old Gobbler was so quiet. We must trust her and the men to take care of themselves."

William said, "I'll look out from the loft. Maybe I can see the Indians from there."

He seemed to fly up the ladder. A moment later he slid down to report. "They are right at the edge of the clearing!"

Rachel could not hold back a sob. She dearly loved Aunt Callie.

"There's no time to waste crying!" Mrs. Donelson said sharply to her little daughter. "Perhaps we can frighten the savages away. If we have to shoot them down, we will. You and Jane must keep us supplied with shot."

She seized a musket, loaded it and thrust it through one of the narrow slots in the wall. The boys had already loaded their guns and fixed them in place. They were sighting along the barrels, through the narrow slots.

Sam was very excited. This was the first Indian attack since he had learned to use a gun. He wanted badly to shoot an Indian, but was ashamed to find his knees shaking.

Rachel knew it was important for each person to have plenty of shot and powder. Jane was getting out the bullet molds. Rachel took the leather bag of bullets around the room.

As she divided them among her brothers and her mother, she noticed that Sam's teeth were chattering. She knew he was frightened and was trying very hard to be brave.

"Sh-shall w-w-we shoot f-f-first?" he asked.

But John said, "No, we shouldn't waste a shot. Wait until they crawl out from under cover. Look! There's the first. There's another! . . ."

At once several shots rang out from the house. The first Indian yelled and leaped up, dropping his gun. His arm had been hurt. He turned and ran into the forest. The other took shelter behind a tree and opened fire.

Leven, who was frightened, began to cry. Rachel hurried over to kiss him and comfort him.

Just then Indian bullets thudded against the back of the house. The savages had surrounded it.

Rachel had run to a chink in one shutter and was peering out.

"Mother! I see two Indians in the barnyard. They're going to the stables!"

Mrs. Donelson rushed to Rachel's window. "They're after the horses. Heaven help poor Somerset! If he's still in the stables, they'll surely kill him. Boys, shoot from this side."

At the same moment William and John fired. One of the savages staggered a few steps before he fell. The other screamed in pain. Another Indian darted out and dragged the injured man into the thicket. Everybody in the house waited tensely. They wondered how many more Indians were hiding among the bushes.

After a little while Rachel's sharp ears caught a sound. "They're leaving! I hear hoofbeats."

"You hear the hoofbeats of *our* horses," William said grimly.

Sure enough, there was movement in the thicket on the edge of the yard. The Indians were leading Mr. Donelson's two work horses away.

Rachel was worried about Old Gobbler. "Will they take our cows and chickens, too?"

"No. Indians generally want only the horses," her mother answered.

"Maybe we can save the horses yet." William took careful aim and fired. It frightened the horses. One reared, jerking his head, pulling the halter out of the Indian's hand. The Indian grabbed for it. But John fired and struck the man in the arm. The savage ducked and disappeared, as the frightened horse galloped back to the stables.

The second thief dashed deeper into the woods, pulling Dolly, the other horse, behind him. In a moment the Donelsons heard hoofbeats, gradually fading away. Evidently the Indians had hidden other horses in the woods before they crept toward the clearing.

"Well," John said, "we certainly wounded three of them badly, and lost only one horse."

"Thank God no one of us was injured or killed!" Mrs. Donelson exclaimed.

Rachel hugged her. "Oh, Mother, you were so brave. I hope I can always be just as brave as you are."

Mrs. Donelson smiled. "If any of you were afraid, you didn't show it."

"I was not very brave inside," Rachel confessed. "I'm glad I wasn't down at the barn!"

"I'd better go to the barn and see if Somerset is all right," John said.

"Let me go see if Aunt Callie is all right!" Rachel exclaimed.

John slid back the bolt on the big door. But William warned, "Don't go out yet. This may be a trick. They may still be waiting in the forest to pay us back. We hurt some of them pretty badly. We don't know how many Indians may be hiding in the forest."

John bolted the door again in a hurry.

"I hope Aunt Callie won't go outside," Rachel said anxiously.

Just then there was a knock on the door. Everyone was startled. Was this a trick of the Indians, too, to make the Donelsons open the door? Had one redskin crept up silently while the others pretended to ride away?

Then they heard Somerset's voice, hoarse with fright. "Let me in! Let me in!" he pleaded . "The Indians have gone, but I'm still scared!"

Rachel hurried to the door, but William was ahead of her. He opened it a crack. Poor Somerset was crouching so close to the door he nearly fell inside. He gave a big sigh of relief.

"Where did you hide?" Rachel cried.

"Yes, how did you escape?" William asked.

"When I heard the shots, I went up to the loft mighty fast. You know the big pine tree near the door, the one with the most branches?"

The boys nodded.

"I got out on a limb and climbed up in the tree. You can hardly see up into the pine. There are dogwoods growing underneath. I climbed up to where the branches were thickest and I sat there in the needles, as still as a bird."

"You were smart to do that, Somerset. You couldn't have saved the horses," Mrs. Donelson said. "And you might have been killed."

"Have the Indians really gone, Somerset?" William asked, "or do you think they're hiding in the woods waiting to attack us again?"

"They're gone. They were scared. There weren't many of them. From up in the pine tree I could see the horses they'd left in the woods. After your last shots they mounted and rode off. One was leading our Dolly. They weren't all able to ride alone. A couple of them needed help. But I can tell you they were leaving—and in a hurry, too!"

The boys laughed.

"Then can't I go see about poor Aunt Callie?" Rachel begged. "I know she's afraid."

Mrs. Donelson nodded. Sam and Rachel dashed across the room and unbolted the door.

The two children ran across the clearing, past the stables and straight to Aunt Callie's cabin. Sam pounded on the door with his fists.

Almost at once there was a terrible *bang!* right in his ear. Sam staggered back.

"Don't shoot, Aunt Callie," Rachel screamed. "It's Sam and me!" The Indians have gone! We just came to see if you were all right."

Inside the cabin Aunt Callie shrieked. The other Donelsons and Somerset and Candis came running across the yard. Mrs. Donelson followed, with Leven in her arms. She called, "Who's shooting?"

Aunt Callie opened the door. An old gun lay on the floor beside her. "Master Sam, I thought you were a wild Indian! I tried to scare you off!"

"You might have killed him." Rachel had turned pale.

"Not with that gun, honey," Aunt Callie said. "It didn't have a thing but some powder in it—powder and a little salt. I use it to chase varmints away from my chickens."

Rachel remembered something. "Oh, my turkey! Did they take Old Gobbler?"

"He's 'way in under the cabin," Aunt Callie said. "I heard him gobble every time there was a shot. He's quieted down now."

Sam laughed heartily, and so did Rachel. They were not afraid any more.

"Come up to the kitchen," Mrs. Donelson said. "We'll all have some hot tea."

There was a great deal of talk while they drank their tea. The boys boasted about how they had shot at the Indians. They praised Somerset for being quick to hide. Aunt Callie said she had been too frightened to do anything but pray.

"I didn't know a thing was happening till I heard the first shots," she said. "I guessed there were Indians about. I was so scared I could hardly walk. But I managed to get my door and windows bolted. Then I got my gun."

"I handed out the bullets!" Rachel reminded them. "I gave out the bullets! I didn't act a bit afraid. I was brave, like Mother."

"Don't brag," said Sam.

That put a damper on Rachel. She hung her head. Aunt Callie patted it. "You were brave, I know, honey, even if you didn't do any shooting. There's a good many other things to do besides the shooting."

Mrs. Donelson smiled at her daughter. "It was Rachel who kept the baby quiet."

Rachel felt happier. "I guess I didn't do much, but I helped a little, didn't I?"

"We all did our parts," said Mrs. Donelson, "and your father will be proud of us."

The turkey strutted up to the door and looked in. Sometimes he got a piece of bread after dinner. "*Gobble-gobble-gobble!*" he said.

"Isn't he a fine pet! We'll never eat him now, will we, Mother?" Rachel looked at him proudly as she tossed him a bit of hoecake.

"No, indeed. If he hadn't warned us, I might not have known the Indians were coming—until too late! We are very lucky."

Everybody looked solemn as they thought this over. They realized that they were very lucky to be alive and not even hurt.

"Here, Rachel," said Sam. "Give him this piece too. I reckon he deserves something special. I won't ever tease you about him again. Maybe he was the real hero of the Indian fight."

Everybody laughed.

The Gift

SAM ran through the big barn, trying to dodge Severn. They were playing soldiers. They had heard that the colonies were going to war with England.

"Bang!" cried Severn. "I shot you! You're dead, you dirty redcoat!"

Sam clutched at his heart and collapsed into a pile of hay. "Just you wait," he said, as he got to his feet. "I may be dead, but other soldiers will take my place. King George will send a lot of ships and men over the sea to fight the colonists."

"This would be a better game with more colonists. Let's get Rachel." Severn said.

He sat on the hay and laid down the stick he used for a musket. "She can be the redcoat, and you and I can both be Americans."

"All right," Sam agreed. "I'll call her."

Rachel was playing with the dogs in the yard. When she heard her brother's shout she hurried to the barn. She loved to have a part in the exciting games Sam and Severn played.

The boys gave her a stick-gun and explained that she was the English army.

"Now, Rachel, you stay on this side of the hay. Sam and I will go around to the other side and the battle will begin."

"But why do we have to fight?" Rachel asked. She had heard her father speak of the war with England. She knew her big brothers had joined the militia. But she did not really understand what the war was about. She didn't see why the British and the Americans wanted to fight each other.

"Father says it's because King George will not treat us like Englishmen," said Severn. "Father explained it to me. He says the King wants to tax all sorts of things, but he doesn't want to send enough money from England to help us. And he doesn't want us to have anything to say about the taxes we pay or our laws . . . or something," he ended, frowning.

Severn was nearly twelve years old but not very good at explaining a revolution.

"Well, I don't like to fight wars. Let's think of some other game." She sat down in the hay beside Severn. Just then they heard their sister.

"Rachel," Jane was calling, "Mother wants you. She says to hurry."

"Oh, dear!" Rachel exclaimed. "I have to leave. Mother is going to visit old Mrs. Johnson and she wants me to ride with her."

"Well," Severn said, "we can play when you come back."

"I wish I were a boy." Rachel sighed as she brushed the hay from her dress. "Mother never takes you or Sam to visit the sick or carry food to hungry people."

She ran out of the barn quickly. Her mother did not like to be kept waiting.

Soon Rachel and Mrs. Donelson were riding down the trail. Bushes were green with little new leaves. The sun shone brightly, and birds sang from every tree. Rachel's pony, Duke, pranced and tossed his head. He did not want to trot on a fine morning. Rachel too wanted to go flying down the trail. But instead she had to trot sedately beside her mother. Mrs. Donelson never let her horse gallop.

Rachel thought about the boys. How much she would like to be playing in the barn with them! She knew her mother hoped she would be neighborly, but Rachel did not enjoy these visits. Unfortunate people made her unhappy.

Rachel could tell that few people used this trail. It was rough and overgrown with weeds and bushes. Soon they rode up to a clearing. A tiny log house stood in the center, with a few sheds near by. What a lonely place! Rachel knew she might have to sit still for hours while her mother talked with the invalid.

While they were tying the horses to some trees, the door of the cabin opened. A stocky young man came out. He was on his way to the fields, but he stopped to talk with them. He seemed very glad to see them.

"How's your mother, Tom?"

"She hasn't been doing so well," he answered sadly. "I'm afraid I don't look after the house properly. That worries her. And she's mighty lonesome. At this time of year I have to work in the fields. I can't stay with her."

"You run along to your plowing, Tom. Today my daughter and I will tend your mother."

Tom Johnson thanked her and hurried to his cornfield. Rachel followed her mother into the cabin. It was dark and stuffy. There were muddy tracks on the floor. Things were scattered about untidily.

In a big bed in one corner lay a frail old woman. The bedclothes were rumpled. She looked cross and unhappy.

Rachel felt rather cross, too. She hated to be indoors on any fine spring day. It was much worse to be in a dirty little house with a fretful old woman. She envied her brothers.

Mrs. Donelson explained that she had come to spend the day, so that Tom might finish his plowing. She straightened the quilts.

Mrs. Johnson said gratefully, "You're a good neighbor. I'm so happy to see you and your pretty little daughter. But I hate for you to come into this house. Poor Tom tries hard, but he just doesn't have time to tend to everything."

"Never mind," Mrs. Donelson said soothingly. "I remember how neat you kept this house before you got sick. Rachel and I can soon set it to rights for you."

She opened the front door to let in the sun and air. She handed her daughter a turkey wing. "Sweep up the ashes on the hearth."

Rachel was glad to have something to do. This was one of her tasks at home, and soon she had the hearth clean. She looked about for other work. She began to enjoy herself.

Mrs. Johnson smiled at her. "There are yellow flowers in bloom in back of the cabin. Would you pick some and bring them to me?"

"Oh, yes, ma'am!" Rachel darted out of the house. How good it was to be in the sunshine! She was glad she wasn't sick in bed.

Poor Mrs. Johnson! Rachel's heart was filled with pity. It must be dreadful to be weak and sick and to have to stay in a dirty little house.

"I'll pick her a lot of flowers," Rachel decided. She felt ashamed of the ugly thoughts she had had. She picked a big bunch of the yellow flowers. They were easy to find. They made a big golden patch by the dark woods. "How fresh they smell," she thought."

Bluebells and white foamflowers were blooming in the woods. She picked these also.

She ran back into the cabin. It looked very different already! Sun streamed in. Mrs. Donelson had swept and dusted. The bed had been freshly made with a bright quilt. Mrs. Johnson sat propped up with pillows.

Her face lighted up when she saw the flowers. "What a lovely posy!"

"The yellow ones are beautiful! See the dew on their petals. What kind are they?"

"They're English daffodils," the old lady answered. "I brought them with me from my home across the sea."

"Across the sea?"

Mrs. Johnson explained. "When I was married and left England, I was just a young thing—barely sixteen. I'd heard that America was a wilderness. I hated to leave my mother's lovely garden. So I dug up some daffodils. I put the bulbs in a little cloth bag and hung them around my neck, to be sure I wouldn't lose them.

"We got on a ship and set sail for America. It was wintertime and very cold. The winds howled and the sea was rough. Everybody on board was sick and frightened. Then a terrible storm came up and salt water washed even into the cabin below deck where we slept. I'd put my bag of bulbs in a chest, but they got wet and I was afraid they were ruined.

"It was six weeks before we sighted land. Soon after I reached my new home I planted my daffodils. Nobody knows how glad I was to see them send up green leaves."

"Did they bloom that year?" asked Rachel.

"They bloomed that spring, and they've been blooming every spring since."

"Are these the very same bulbs that you brought from your mother's garden?"

"No, dear, the bulbs have divided many times, and those little bulbs in turn have grown big and divided. I've given away many hundreds but I've taken a few with me every time I've moved."

She smiled at Rachel. "Why don't you pick more of the daffodils to take home? And this fall I'll give you some bulbs. You can plant them and then, when you marry, perhaps you'll take them to your own home."

Rachel's dark eyes shone. She would love to have a garden of beautiful flowers like these. She hoped her daffodils would grow fast.

"That's very kind of you, Mrs. Johnson," said Mrs. Donelson. "Now, Rachel, I want you to help me prepare the food we brought."

Soon they all had steaming bowls of soup.

"How delicious this tastes!" Mrs. Johnson smiled gratefully. "Poor Tom isn't much of a cook. He does his best, though."

"There are other things in that basket," Mrs. Donelson said. "Tom will find it easy to warm them for you."

"Oh, how good Mother is!" Rachel thought. "She has made Mrs. Johnson comfortable. And she made Tom stop worrying. She's made this little house seem light and cozy. I hope I can be just like Mother."

The Donelsons stayed all afternoon. The two women sewed bright squares for a new quilt. Rachel chattered to the old lady. Mrs. Johnson told stories of her early days in America. After a long while Rachel went out to pick another bunch of daffodils.

When she came back, her mother said, "The day has flown! Now we must be on our way."

"I'm sorry to see you go. But Tom will soon be in from the fields to look after me. You've been mighty kind, Mrs. Donelson. And having Rachel here made me especially happy."

"Oh, I've had a good time!" Rachel cried.

"You're a dear child to have kept an old woman company. I want to give you something," Mrs. Johnson went on. "Over there on the dresser are a little brass candlestick and a snuffer. I brought them with me from England, too. I'd like you to have them."

Rachel admired the quaint little candlestick and snuffer. "Oh, how pretty! Thank you so much. I'll keep them always." She reached up and kissed the old lady.

"We must hurry," said Mrs. Donelson. "The shadows are growing long."

"Good-by," Mrs. Johnson called from her bed. "Thank you for all you have done. Come again soon, both of you."

"I will," Rachel answered, and waved once more before she closed the door.

As they rode down the trail, Rachel sniffed at her bunch of daffodils. She thought about the dear little candlestick in her mother's saddlebag. It hadn't been such an unpleasant day after all. In fact, she would like to visit Mrs. Johnson now and then and clean her house.

"Rachel," said Mrs. Donelson, "I was pleased with the way you behaved today. You really helped to cheer old Mrs. Johnson up. And I know you would much rather have stayed at home. I realize that you were having a good time playing with your brothers."

Rachel thought for a moment. "Why, Mother," she said in surprise, "I believe I enjoyed it more than playing with the boys today. I'd like to go back to see her again soon. Making other people happy is right nice, isn't it? It makes you feel good inside."

Mrs. Donelson looked down at her daughter and smiled. "I hope you remember that the next time you quarrel with Severn or Sam—or the next time I ask you to take care of the baby."

Rachel's face turned pink. "I'll try to," she said in a small voice. "Maybe the candlestick will help me remember," she added hopefully.

Outdoor Cooking

EARLY in the spring of 1776 John and William Donelson rode away to the county seat to drill with the militia.

"Father, what is the militia?" Rachel asked, after she had waved good-by to her brothers.

He sat down by the fire and took Rachel on his lap. She was nearly nine years old, but she still liked to sit on her father's knee.

"The militia is a kind of army," he explained. "The men who join it are usually farmers or tradesmen. They can't stay with the army all the time. But they must be ready to fight if they are called on.

"So John and William have gone to learn the things soldiers must know. Then, when they are needed, they'll be good soldiers."

"But why must they be soldiers at all?" Rachel asked. "Why do we have to fight?"

"Because we're in a war against England. Virginia used to be one of England's colonies. Now we have declared our independence and a revolution has started."

He smiled at Rachel's puzzled face. "You see, this country was settled by people from other countries. Remember the story of Captain John Smith? Before the first English colonists founded Jamestown, there were only Indians in America. The settlers came," he went on, "because they wanted to be free. They longed to think as they wished, and to say what they thought. They wanted liberty and happiness in a new land, and a chance to earn a good living. Do you understand?"

Rachel leaned against her father and nodded. He stroked her hair fondly. "Now the King of England wishes to tell us what to do, when he doesn't know what we really need. He's too far away to understand conditions here. He wants us to pay taxes, though we had no part in levying them. He wants to dictate to us. We don't like that— and we'll fight for freedom!"

Mr. Donelson's voice rang out strong and proud. Rachel sat up straight and said, "Yes, we should fight."

Her father laughed. "You're a true pioneer girl. Our new country will need brave women as well as brave men."

Several days later Mr. Donelson said at breakfast, "Sam, I'll take you to the woods with me today. My land beyond Sandy Creek must be surveyed. It's high time you learned how to survey. Every man who owns land should know exactly where his land begins and ends."

"Oh, Father," Rachel cried, "may I go, too?"

"What could you do in the woods?"

"I—I . . . maybe I could help you and Sam," Rachel answered lamely.

"You couldn't walk that far." Sam knew his sister hated to be left behind. But surveying was a man's job. Sam wanted to act like a man.

Rachel was disappointed, but then she had an inspiration. "I could cook for you!" she suggested. "Aunt Callie has taught me a lot about cooking. She says I'm a good cook."

Sam looked more approving, and her father could not help laughing. "Come along then. We'll be glad to have a cook for company. But you must walk as far as we do. And you mustn't complain, no matter how tired you are."

Rachel ran out to the kitchen, where Aunt Callie helped her find supplies. Mr. Donelson packed them and his surveying instruments in the saddlebags of the horse he would lead.

Rachel was relieved to see the horse. Now she would not have to carry the food. If she got really tired, surely Father would let her ride.

He and Sam both carried their guns. They might meet an Indian or, Sam said, a bear. He kept on talking about bears. It was time for them to come out of their dens. After sleeping all winter they would be hungry. And they might have little cubs with them. A mother bear would fight to protect her young. She would be even more dangerous than a male.

But Rachel was not worried. It was so pretty in the woods. Bluebells were in bloom. The scent of wild honeysuckle was wonderful. A rabbit hopped across the path.

Rachel was surprised when they reached Sandy Creek. She wasn't a bit tired. She was having a wonderful time.

Mr. Donelson set up his stakes and chain. He showed Sam how to measure with them.

Rachel found a patch of white violets. As she picked them she could hear Sam call figures for his father to write down.

She sat down on a log and sorted out her violets to make a nosegay. Around the flowers she put a circle of dark-green leaves. They looked very pretty. She tied the nosegay with a long piece of grass. Then she laid it gently in the stream. It would stay fresh there, and she would take it home to Mother.

She knelt by the stream and let the water ripple through her fingers. Then she began to build a little dam of pebbles.

Suddenly she heard her father call, "Daughter! It's time to start a fire."

He and Sam came back, looking hot and hungry. Rachel told herself she would cook a good meal for them. Sam helped her gather some dry bark and dead leaves. Then he kindled the fire with his flint and steel.

Rachel watched him strike the flint hard with the piece of steel until a spark flew out. The first two or three sparks died, but finally one caught a leaf. Sam bent down and blew gently on it. A tiny flame grew and caught another leaf. Soon there was a cracking fire.

Mr. Donelson brought dry wood to add to it. "Call us when you're ready," he said. Then he and Sam went back into the woods.

Rachel felt very grown-up cooking dinner for the men. She unpacked the saddlebags. There were slices of meat to fry. She placed some stones in the fire and set the iron skillet on them. Then she put the meat in the skillet.

But the fire began to burn low. She ran for sticks to stuff under the skillet. "I mustn't let this go out," she thought. "It's hard to start a fire with flint and steel. I'd better add some more sticks and build up the fire. I won't have the meal ready on time unless I hurry."

She added more sticks. She was so busy building up the fire that she forgot the meat. In a moment there was a smell of burning.

"Oh, dear!" The meat was scorched on one side. Rachel grabbed up the skillet. She was so upset she nearly spilled the meat.

With a stick she tried to scrape off the charred part. It wouldn't come off. But the other side was still raw. Rachel turned the slices over. "I'll be more careful this time," she said to herself.

She watched the skillet closely. Again the fire died down. Rachel wanted to cry. It was so provoking to have to watch both the meat and the fire! But this time she got the meat cooked nicely—on one side, at least. She set the skillet on a near-by rock.

Then she remembered about bread. Aunt Callie had told her to bake corn pones. But what could she mix them in? The skillet was full of fried meat. She needed another pan.

Rachel looked in the saddlebag again, but there was no other pan. She pushed the meat to one side of the skillet. From the leather sack Aunt Callie had given her she poured in the corn meal. She took the skillet over to the stream and dipped up some water. Then she put the skillet back on the fire and tried to mix the corn meal with the water.

Suddenly the water steamed up and burned her wrist. Rachel nearly dropped the skillet. Corn-meal batter ran all over the meat. Smoke blew in her eyes. Her wrist hurt. The batter was too moist. It bubbled up over the meat.

As branches crackled, Rachel glanced up quickly. Suppose a mother bear had smelled the food and brought her cubs to get it! What could she do? But it was only her father and Sam.

"Isn't our dinner ready yet?" Mr. Donelson asked, peering into the skillet. "What's this you made—Yorkshire pudding?"

Rachel's lips quivered. "There—there was no bowl to mix the batter in."

Sam, too, peered into the skillet. "It's certainly *mixed* now!" He laughed.

Rachel bit her lower lip to stop its trembling, but could not hold back two big tears that slid down her cheeks.

"There, there! You didn't claim to be a woodsman—only a kitchen cook. Let me see if I can turn this pudding over and make a big hoecake of it. I like hoecakes."

Father took out his hunting knife and slid it around the edge of the skillet. With a twist of his wrist he flipped the mixture over. It fell back into the skillet and was soon cooked on the other side. Rachel watched it hopefully.

It didn't look quite so messy now.

The batter was brown and the meat was well done. Mr. Donelson cut the hoecake into three big wedges, and put them on pieces of pine bark.

"Now if we just had some salt," Sam said, "this might not be bad." He bit into the hoecake and then looked surprised. Aunt Callie had thought to add salt to the corn meal. The hoecake was good! Rachel's spirits lifted a little.

"Food always tastes better when its cooked and eaten outdoors," Mr. Donelson said.

"Even when it's mixed up and burned?" Rachel asked in a low voice.

"Why, that's the way one discovers new ways to prepare food," her father said. "I'll tell you what happened to me when I first cooked outdoors. I was about sixteen and had gone out surveying. Usually a friend went with me, an older man who did the cooking. But this day I was alone. I was enjoying myself. I'd done a lot of work. Everything had gone well."

"I'd shot a young turkey. I put it on a spit over the fire to roast it. It smelled so good! And I was hungry. The turkey was almost done.

"All of a sudden, from the woods, came a big wolf! Before I could grab my gun he had seized the turkey and made off with it. I was too surprised to move.

"I had no other food with me. I hunted, but I couldn't find even a squirrel to shoot. So I just had to finish surveying and go home without any dinner—not even a hoecake."

Sam laughed, but Rachel looked sorry. "Oh, Father, were you starving?"

He shook his head. "I was young and healthy. It didn't hurt me to miss a meal. I've often missed one since. . . . Well, Sam, back to work."

Sam licked his fingers, but Rachel went to the stream to wash her hands. In the cold water her burned wrist throbbed. Sam told her how to make a mud poultice for it. The cool wet mud took out some of the pain.

"We have about an hour's work left to do. Will you be lonely, Rachel?"

"Oh. no, Father! "I'll play here by the creek."

When they had gone she scrubbed the skillet out with sand and rinsed it well. She put it back in the saddlebag. The horse was cropping the thick grass along the stream.

As she worked Rachel thought about her father. Most men would have complained about burned, soggy food. Sam would probably have made a fuss about it all the rest of the day. But her father had known how to make the best of it. He'd even told that story just to make her feel better. And he'd never tell them at home what a bad cook she was. Neither would Sam. He might tease, but he'd never tell.

Rachel wished she could make them proud of her. Why hadn't she paid more attention to Aunt Callie's cooking lessons? From now on she'd remember everything Aunt Callie taught her.

"I'm going to be the best cook on the Banister River," she promised herself.

Woman's Work

ONE bright morning in the fall of 1778 all the young Donelsons were excited and gay—all except Rachel.

She sat gazing into the fire. Her face was clouded and unhappy. She felt sorry for herself because all her brothers were going to watch the county militia drill. Even Leven, who was only five, was allowed to go.

It was a thrilling thing to see. Besides, Mr. Donelson was a colonel in the militia. Rachel thought that nobody looked so handsome and fine as her father when he rode his big bay horse and taught the young men how to drill.

Rachel had watched them drill a few times. But this morning her mother had said that she must stay at home to help the women with their work, for she had many things to learn.

She had added, "I know you'd rather be with your brothers. But, Rachel, you're too old now to spend all your time playing. Someday you'll have a home of your own. You'll need to know how to keep house. Even if you have servants, you must know how to teach them. Now, when you're a little girl, is the time to learn about housekeeping. You'll be glad someday."

Rachel sighed. Mother was right, of course. She thought over some of the things she had already learned:

How to make candles—enough each fall to last through the dark winter.

How to get lye from ashes to make soap.

How to spin wool and flax and weave the thread into cloth.

How to pluck down from geese and ducks for pillows and comforters.

How to sew.

How to do housework of every sort.

She had enjoyed most of these tasks. But she wanted so much to see the drill!

Her father came over and stroked her dark, curly hair. "Don't sulk, daughter. Our young men aren't drilling for fun. It's their duty. It's your duty to stay here and learn what your mother can teach you. How could men plow the land or fight to protect it if they didn't have womenfolk to provide their food and clothes? Women's work is just as important as men's work. Never forget that, Rachel."

Rachel hadn't thought of that. She felt rather ashamed to have looked so sulky.

Then Somerset brought the horses up from the stables. The men and boys rode off in a cloud of dust. Rachel sighed.

Mrs. Donelson and Aunt Callie had gone out into the yard. Sully sang as she washed the breakfast dishes. She was a Negro girl who helped in the kitchen. She had a sweet, soft voice and Rachel liked to hear her sing. But the song did not cheer her today.

"I wish I'd been born a boy!" she thought. "Boys don't have to stay at home. I might even belong to the militia! I'd be an officer and ride a fine black horse!"

Her father had told her that militiamen must be brave. At this moment Rachel felt full of courage. She also felt very important.

Out in the yard a wren sang in the persimmon trees. Two hound puppies growled and yipped at each other as they played. But in the house it was quiet. The fire crackled softly. Rachel was lost in dreams.

Then her mother called, "Rachel! Come and help Aunt Callie!"

Rachel jumped up guiltily and rushed out.

Aunt Callie sat on the bench under an old oak tree. By her side were two large baskets of apples and several pans.

"These are the last of our fruit," Mrs. Donelson told Rachel. "I want you to help peel and slice them for drying. We'll have to hurry because every minute counts. If the autumn rains begin before the apples are dry we'll have to bring them indoors, and they'll not be so good."

"Here's a sharp knife, honey," Aunt Callie said. "Sit down here by me. You peel and I'll slice. Later we'll change jobs."

Rachel began to feel better. At least this work could be done outdoors. It was pleasant here under the big tree. The air was brisk but not cold.

"Isn't it a lovely day!" She took a deep breath. "I can smell autumn already. And the sun's so bright! It makes all the oak leaves look freshly painted. I like fall."

The old woman smiled. "It's a mighty good day to get things done, too."

Rachel laughed and sat down. She took a big red apple from one basket. She held it to her nose and sniffed. It smelled wonderful! How Leven would like it! She carved two eyes and a nose and mouth on one side of the apple, as she often did to amuse him.

"Don't play, Rachel." Mrs. Donelson set another basket beside her. "We haven't time. Start peeling at once. Put the peelings in this basket. They'll make fine food for the pigs."

Rachel wondered why her sister wasn't working. "Where's Jane?" she asked.

"On the barn roof. She has gone up for the apples that have already dried."

Rachel looked toward the barn. On the gently sloping roof Jane was gathering up the fruit prepared earlier in the week. Her skirts blew out, and her blond hair shone in the sun.

Rachel knew that the apples were put in a high place to keep ants or small animals from eating them. The roof of the barn was right over the loft where Somerset slept. If a larger animal like a possum or a bear should climb up at night after the fruit, Somerset would hear it. He would get up and frighten it away.

"How wonderful to be up on the roof!" she thought. "I could see all over the farm, perhaps even over the trees."

She laid down the knife and the half-peeled apple. "Oh, Mother, can't I go and help Jane? I've always wanted to climb up to the roof. Don't you think I'm big enough? I'm eleven now."

Mrs. Donelson looked stern. "Daughter, daughter!" She shook her head. "You must finish the task at hand. Haven't I taught you that? Do first what is in front of you!" Then she, too, sat down on the bench and began to help Aunt Callie prepare the apples.

Rachel flushed. She hated to have her mother chide her. Tears pricked her eyelids but she winked hard and held them back.

"Why can't Jane peel the apples?" she muttered. "Why do I have to do everything?"

Her mother did not answer. She knew Rachel did not like any work that kept her still. Yet the child must learn to stay at a task.

"When we have sliced all these," she said presently, "you and Sully may spread them on the roof. Let's save enough apples to make a pie, Callie," she added.

"Ummmm!" said Rachel. "May I help make its?" Wasn't she going to be the best cook on Banister River?

"We'd better make two," Aunt Callie said. "We'll not have any more fresh apples this year."

It seemed to Rachel that she peeled for hours. Finally she picked up the last apple.

Just then Jane and Somerset brought the baskets of dried apples from the barn.

"We're through with this lot!" Rachel called. "Mother says I may help spread them on the roof. I'm coming up right away. Sully will bring up the apples."

"I have to put these dried apples in bags first." Jane shivered a little. "You'd better wear a shawl. It's colder up there in the wind."

Rachel ran toward the kitchen calling, "Sully! Come help me spread apples on the roof. And please bring me a shawl."

Somerset carried the baskets of freshly sliced apples to the barn. He climbed up the ladder and set them on the roof. Then he took the peelings to feed the pigs.

Aunt Callie fetched a little bucket. She filled it with apples for the pies.

"Please don't make the pies until I come down!" Rachel called back as she hurried to the barn. "I want to help."

Governor Patrick Henry

IT WAS windy but lovely up on the barn. Rachel held her brown curls back and stared out over the plantation. She had never been able to see so much land from one place.

"Look, Sully! You can see the corn 'way down by the river! You can see the whole place—clear to the farthest field. I can even see where the road turns, and that's nearly a mile away!"

"Rachel! Don't get too near the edge!" cried her mother. "Be careful!"

The roof sloped so gently that it was easy to walk up it. Rachel knew her mother was watching to see that they didn't waste time.

She bent over one basket and took out a handful of the pale round apple slices. She began to lay them on the roof.

"You start at one end and I'll start at this," she suggested to Sully, who was nearer the other basket. "Mother told me to lay them in straight rows over the roof."

"I don't see what difference it makes," Sully said "as long as they're all laid out flat. We mustn't put one on top of another."

"You do it more evenly if you make rows." Rachel bent over the gray roof, and placed the little circles carefully one below another. "If you just lay them down helter-skelter some are bound to get on top of others. Then they won't dry."

For a while it was quiet on the roof. The two girls worked fast. Now and then one stood up. Their backs ached from stooping. At last the roof was almost covered with the apple slices. The baskets were empty.

Rachel ate the last slice. Then she climbed down the ladder, while Sully threw the baskets down to Somerset.

Now for the apple pie!

Rachel skipped across the yard to the kitchen. Aunt Callie was already there, and had mixed the pastry. Jane sat on a bench, stuffing dried apples into cloth sacks. Somerset would hang these from the rafters in the loft. It would smell of apples throughout the winter. Rachel dropped her shawl on the bench and put on a big apron.

"Please let me roll out the crust!"

Aunt Callie smiled at her. She got down the rolling pin and the flat board on which she made bread. She took the lump of dough from the bowl and laid it on the board.

"Get it all," Rachel urged. "Every bit!"

White flour was too precious to waste a speck. And an apple pie would be a real treat, a grand change from puddings made with corn meal.

When all the dough was scraped out, Rachel seized the rolling pin. She rolled this way and that, trying to smooth out the dough.

"Try to roll in just one direction, honey," Aunt Callie advised. "You'll get better pie crust." At last Rachel had a thin, smooth, even sheet of dough, just like Aunt Callie's.

"We'll cut it in half," Aunt Callie said, "and make two big pies."

With a sharp knife Rachel divided the dough. Aunt Callie asked, "Can you lift one piece and put it in the pan?"

Rachel had never done that but she was eager to try. She slipped her hands under the smooth sheet. Carefully . . . carefully she lifted it. She laid it on the deep pan. Gently she pressed it in, against the sides and bottom. She had done it! She had not torn or wrinkled it.

She felt very proud. "Now let me put the apples in! I'll make them even."

Aunt Callie put the other piece of pastry in another deep pan. "We must divide the apples between them," she said. She gave Rachel the bucket of apples.

Rachel laid a few slices at a time in each pan, saying, "Some for you and some for you. Some for you and some for you!"

At last the pans were full. Aunt Callie showed her how to put a big lump of butter on the apples. Then she took a jug and poured honey over them.

Rachel watched with delight. How good it would be! She was tired of sweets that tasted of molasses. "I can't wait to eat it!"

"I reckon you'll have to. We can't eat till the menfolks come, and that'll be about two o'clock."

Rachel groaned, and Jane and Aunt Callie laughed at her.

"Let me finish the other one all by myself," Rachel begged.

After the second pie was made she looked at it with pride. Then she slipped both pies into the oven built in the side of the fireplace. She waited impatiently for them to bake.

It seemed a long time before Father and the boys came home. Aunt Callie and Sully had a fine dinner ready for them of stewed chicken, field peas and rice, salad greens—and of course one of the delicious apple pies.

After the good meal was over Colonel Donelson said, "I heard that Patrick Henry is somewhere nearby."

"The Governor?" his wife said in surprise. "Why is he in this neighborhood?"

"I'm not sure. My friends say he's looking over the land to see how it can be used best. But he may be on some secret military business."

"Will he come to our house?" Rachel asked. "I'd love to see the Governor!"

"Me too!" said Sam.

"If he did, perhaps we could have a little music, or hunting," William said jokingly. "Some of the militiamen told me the Governor will drop almost any business to play the fiddle. And he loves a fox hunt or a coon hunt better than most men."

"I doubt if he has much time now for fiddling," Colonel Donelson said. "He's busy making speeches about the war—and very good speeches, too. He's a fine orator and a fine Governor. If anyone can lead us through these trying times of revolution he can."

"I wish he had come to dinner," Rachel said. "Then he could have had a piece of my pie."

"And perhaps he would have made a speech to you," Severn teased.

"Don't jest about his speeches," their father said gravely. "I've told you how stirring they are. I'll never forget how he said 'Give me liberty or give me death!' "

"I didn't mean to jest about his speeches," Severn protested. "I know we're lucky to have such a fine speaker for governor."

"He's led Virginia to rebel against Great Britain," Colonel Donelson said. "Now he's doing all he can to help us gain freedom for the colonies here in America."

The family was still talking at the table when two horsemen rode up.

Colonel Donelson and his sons stepped out into the yard to greet them. Rachel went to the door with her mother and Jane. Who could these strangers be?

She was delighted to hear her father say, "Governor Henry! Welcome to my house! Won't you come in and rest? Mrs. Donelson will find something for you and your companion to eat."

Patick Henry! The very name was exciting! Rachel peeped from behind Jane to have a look at the famous patriot.

She was curious to see the man who had cried, "Give me liberty or give me death," but who liked best to play the fiddle or to hunt.

Patrick Henry was a fine-looking man. His blue eyes twinkled under heavy brows. He had a friendly smile.

Each member of the family was introduced. Rachel made a deep curtsy to the Governor and another to his aide.

"I've seen many lovely things on this trip," the Governor said to her father, "but none lovelier than the ladies of your house." He was looking at Rachel's dark curls and sparkling brown eyes.

"Please do not flatter her," Colonel Donelson murmured. "I am afraid we may spoil her."

Mrs. Donelson had called Sully to clear the table. Then the girl brought in cool buttermilk, part of a roast chicken and a loaf of bread.

Rachel tugged at her mother's sleeve. "The other apple pie, Mother," she whispered.

Mrs. Donelson went to the kitchen herself to get the pie. Proudly she set it on the table before the Governor.

"My word!" cried Patrick Henry. "What's this wonderful creation?"

Rachel knew that he was joking. Both he and his aide were smiling. But they looked hungrily at the pie, too.

"This is Rachel's first pie," her mother explained. "She wants you to have it, Governor Henry. I know what a fearless man you are, but I really think your life is not in danger."

Governor Henry rose. He did not crack a smile. Instead, he made a deep bow. "I've never been so honored," he said to Rachel. "But I'd be selfish to eat it here. An apple pie baked in an oven would be manna to my staff."

"If I have your permission, Miss Rachel," he added, "I'll take this pie to camp—though heaven knows how I'll get it there!"

The Governor's aide sprang up. "I'll be glad to carry it!" he said loudly.

Patrick Henry threw back his head and shouted with laughter. "You see, my dear." He bowed to Rachel again. "I think any one of my men would crawl to camp with that pie on his back, to get a share."

"It's a good pie, all right." Sam hated to see it go—even to the Governor.

Colonel Donelson nodded. "My daughter," he said proudly, "is a fine cook."

Mrs. Donelson put the pie in a basket. "It will be easier to carry the pan in this."

"We'll return both the pan and the basket," Patrick Henry said. He knew how hard it was to get such things in the backwoods.

A few minutes later the Governor and his aide left the Donelson clearing. Rachel stood in the doorway watching until they were out of sight. Then she gave a little skip of joy. She had made her parents proud of her. She had baked a pie for the great Governor!

Farewell to Virgina

ONE very hot afternoon nearly a year later Colonel Donelson and John came home from a business trip. They brought William who had married and now had a farm of his own.

At the supper table that night Colonel Donelson told his family a piece of very exciting news.

"We're going to leave Virginia," he announced. "All the money I invested in the ironworks has been lost. A group of settlers plan to move west to the Great French Salt Lick on the Cumberland River. The land there is especially good for farming. The chances for business of all kinds are better."

Rachel could hardly believe it. Why, she had never had any other home! She and most of her brother and sisters had been born and reared in this house. She looked out the open door to the yard. In the evening light the trees were softly green. The flowers she and Jane had planted and tended were blooming.

How could they bear to leave the garden and the house? It might stand empty and nobody would enjoy the blossoms. She was sure that the house would be lonely without the Donelsons.

Rachel was not sure she wished to go on such a long journey. Home was too dear. The Cumberland River was 'way beyond the western mountains.

But Sam was full of eager questions. He wanted to know all about the plans.

"We'll stay first at a cabin near the Holston River," Colonel Donelson explained. "Some of the men will go there at once."

"Why will we stay at the cabin instead of going on our journey?" Sam asked.

"We have to build a number of large flatboats to carry our goods down the rivers," the Colonel explained. "Then we'll journey down the Holston River to the Tennessee, and on the Tennessee to the Ohio, and on the Ohio to the Cumberland, and up the Cumberland."

"But, Father," Sam asked, "won't that be dangerous? Silas Perkins down the road told me there were lots of Indians all along the Holston. His uncle was killed there. He said the river was so treacherous nobody could travel on it."

"I think we can," Colonel Donelson said. "Some of the men will drive the livestock—our cattle and horses—over the Wilderness Trail. That's really a more dangerous route."

"You won't go that way will you, Father?" Rachel asked quickly. "You'll be with Mother and the rest of us, won't you?"

Colonel Donelson smiled at her. "Yes, I'll go by the river with the flatboats."

John said, "Father is to be in charge of the river journey. Captain James Robertson will take the party overland."

Rachel looked at her father with pride. He had been chosen to lead the expedition!

"James Robertson is a good man for the job," William put in. "I guess he and Daniel Boone know as much about that part of the country as any living men."

"Yes," Colonel Donelson agreed, "and the Indians know he is a fearless fighter. He has shown his courage in many a border battle. We'll meet him at the Great French Salt Lick."

"What's a French Lick?" Rachel's voice was scornful. "Lick" was such an ugly word.

"Why, Rachel," said her father, "you know a lick is a place where there's an unusual amount of salt in the earth."

"Wild animals come to lick the ground, for all living creatures need salt," Sam explained. "Men go there for salt, too, when they discover places where animals have found it."

"French explorers found this particular place, so it's called the Great French Salt Lick," said Colonel Donelson.

"Is the river really so treacherous?" his wife asked fearfully.

"There will be high waters in the early spring, when snow melts. At that time we can get over the rocks and shoals without much trouble. As for the Indians, Governor Henry sent Colonel Evan Shelby to get rid of them earlier this year. He and his men destroyed villages along the Tennessee River. They wiped out Chickamauga Town and Chattanooga Town on the riverbank. The Indians may hesitate to attack us at this time. If they do, we have forty brave men with us to fight them."

He smiled reassuringly at his wife, then turned to Sam. "And if the journey is dangerous, my boy? I hope you're not suggesting that we pass up this chance to move to the West because of a few risks. We cannot avoid risks."

Sam's face turned very red. He couldn't bear to have his father think he was a coward. "I was thinking of Mother," he mumbled, "and the girls. I'm not afraid."

Colonel Donelson reached over and rumpled Sam's hair. "I know you're a brave boy. You've proved it many times. And your mother is brave. I doubt if she or your sisters will be cowed by any adventure which may befall us."

Sam grinned, feeling better because his father understood how he felt.

Colonel Donelson's eyes twinkled. "As a matter of fact, Rachel is always longing for adventure. Sometimes she has begged me to take her traveling. Now she may have both her wishes."

It was Rachel's turn to blush. But she had never dreamed of a journey like this! "Perhaps the Indians have come back to their towns along the river," she said, with a shiver.

"Indians are not our greatest hazard," her father said. "A few may have strayed back to their old homes. But after we pass those towns we come to the hard part of the trip."

"Could anything be more dangerous than Indians?" Rachel asked.

"Yes. There's a high mountain by the Tennessee River, just at Chattanooga Town. It's called the Lookout. It got its name because travelers on the river must begin there to look out for the terrible Suck, the Shoals and the Skillet."

Rachel wondered at the strange names! What on earth, she thought, was a river Skillet? Shoals, she knew, were swift, shallow waters where a boat could get caught on the rocks. Suck she could guess at. But a skillet was a frying pan.

Her father could see that she was puzzled. He laughed, leaned over and gave her hand a little squeeze. "The Suck is a deep place in the river between two high bluffs. The current there is very rapid. A boat may be swamped and lost."

"Or dashed against the bluffs," William added.

"But what is the skillet?" Rachel asked.

"The Skillet and the Boiling Pot," her father explained, "are names of other bad places. The water in the Skillet bubbles and hisses. The water at the Pot seems to boil."

"Dear me!" Rachel exclaimed.

She sat still after that for a long time, listening. The men talked of supplies for the expedition. They discussed how long it might take to build a big flatboat.

"We must send all the food we can harvest and prepare," said Mrs. Donelson. "Enough for a whole year. And I must make new clothes for all the younger boys."

Still Rachel said nothing. A river where water boiled and hissed would be very different from the Banister.

"This isn't my idea of a journey at all!" she thought. "Oh, that dreadful Skillet!"

The next weeks were the busiest Rachel had ever known. Every member of the household worked from dawn until long after dark.

The family had to take everything they could to the new home. They must harvest all their crops, for there would be no cleared fields or garden waiting for them. They made extra soap and candles, much earlier than usual. The womenfolk had extra weaving and sewing to do.

"Will we send Old Gobbler with Mr. Robertson?" Rachel asked one morning.

"All the fowls will go by flatboat," her mother answered. "They couldn't stand the long trip overland. But I'm afraid Old Gobbler is too old to travel either way."

Rachel looked upset. "We—we won't eat him, will we, Mother?" Her voice trembled.

"No, dear, I promise you we won't." Mrs. Donelson smiled. "He's far too tough now, anyway. We had best leave him for the Johnsons."

"But will they keep him?" Though Rachel was over twelve her eyes filled with tears. She had made a pet of Old Gobbler so long.

"We'll explain to Tom Johnson that he is a pet," Mrs. Donelson promised. "And I'll also tell him that he's too tough. He has walked miles through these woods till he's hard as flint!"

Rachel laughed. "I'm glad of that!"

It was not yet daylight on this gray November morning. Mrs. Donelson was busy packing the last things in the house.

"Come, children, finish your breakfast," she urged. Hastily Rachel took another spoonful of porridge. It was hard to swallow, because she had a lump in her throat.

Somerset had built only a little fire. The house was cold, dark, and strangely empty. Almost everything the Donelsons would take with them was packed on the horses. Somerset was in the stables now, feeding the horses.

The family sat close around the hearth. The firelight shone on their solemn and excited faces. They did not even know how long it would be before they would eat another meal in a house of their own. Mrs. Donelson looked around the big room. It was impossible to take the beds, chairs, and most of the other furniture on the journey. These things were much too heavy and large to be moved by horseback or flatboat. Only a few fine pieces which Mrs. Donelson had brought from her parents' home would be taken.

"How hard it is for Mother to part from so much of our furniture!" Rachel thought.

"May I have a new bed when we get to the French Salt Lick?" asked Leven.

He had been worried to see his brothers carry his bed out of the house. Mrs. Donelson had sent it to his sister Catherine.

"I'll make you a bed and table," William promised. "Fine cherry ones."

"Good!" Leven handed Aunt Callie his empty porridge bowl.

"Did you remember your daffodil bulbs, Rachel?" Mrs. Donelson asked.

"Yes, I didn't forget. I dug them up a long time ago, early in the fall, and I packed them with my clothes." No matter where she lived, she'd always take some of those bulbs.

It made Rachel feel better to think that she was taking along something from the old house. Probably she'd find just as much to like in the new one. Now she was eager to start.

Somerset knocked and then came in from the stables. He shivered and rubbed his hands together. "It's mighty cold out there! You all must wrap up in everything you can wear. I never knew it so cold this time of year. It's going to snow before noon."

"Oh, dear!" Mrs. Donelson sighed. "The journey on horseback will be hard and cold enough without snow."

At last the fires were put out in the kitchen and the house. Wrapped in coats and quilts, the family mounted the horses. Mrs. Donelson carried the silver and pewter in her saddlebags. John carried the family money. It was in a cloth belt tied carefully around his waist. All the horses were loaded with bedding, cooking utensils and small possessions.

Rachel sat on a cushion behind Severn. She turned and looked back at the empty buildings. Day was just breaking. Red streaks broke through the dark in the east.

"Well, Rachel," Severn said, "this is the beginning of your first journey."

Camp Patrick Henry

AT Camp Patrick Henry, near the fort on the Holston River, it was a bitterly cold December. Rachel shivered even though she was wrapped in Sam's greatcoat and a heavy shawl. She walked in quick, jerky steps between the rows of cabins which made up the camp. "My feet are so cold I can't feel them!" she thought.

Her mother had sent her down to the river-bank with a message. Rachel was sure she was going to freeze stiff as a chunk of wood.

Boats and rafts lined the bank of the river. Men and boys were carrying salted meat, barrels of molasses, and bales of clothing.

Some of the men were still hammering and sawing to finish the new boats. Rachel wondered how long it would be before all the goods were loaded and the river trip really started. She hoped it would not be many more weeks. Surely it would not be so cold farther south.

Some of the boats were too far away for her to see, but she knew there were about thirty of the big, awkward boats.

"It's not a very handsome collection," she thought. A flatboat looked to her like a large raft with a cabin built in the middle. On some she saw log railings or fences around the edge of the decks. She supposed these were to keep small children from falling overboard. There were also a few simple rafts and some dugouts with skins stretched like tents over the middle.

"I'd hate to travel in one of those," she said to herself. "I'm glad my father and my brothers know how to do things right!"

She felt proud of the boat the Donelson men had built. It was named the "Adventure." Its cabin was large, but everything they owned had to go in it or on the deck. Inside it everyone must eat and sleep.

When Rachel reached the "Adventure" she saw Severn on the deck. He looked so cold that Rachel felt sorry for him.

"Poor Severn! Your face is really blue. Why can't you all work inside today?"

"Because there's too much to do," he said crossly. "We have to get all these supplies in place." He pointed to the bales and chests heaped high on the deck.

Severn tugged at a heavy chest. "I guess I can't move this one alone. I'll have to call the others to help me. They're working inside."

He went down the short ladder into the cabin. In a moment William and his father appeared. Both looked cold and tired.

"Oh, Father!" Rachel said. "Can't you stop work for one day? Perhaps it won't be so cold tomorrow. You mustn't get sick."

Her father shook his head. "We'd be foolish to loose time here while the water is high and then run into shallow water on the shoals. But why are you down here, child?"

"It's nearly dinnertime. Mother has a nice hot ham and wants you all to come soon to eat it."

Colonel Donelson smiled. "Your mother is worried about us. But I think we'll live through this. We take turns at working on the deck. It's not so bad under shelter, for today we have a small fire in the cabin. Come in and warm yourself. Then we'll all go back to dinner."

Rachel walked across the wide planks that led from the shore to the deck. William and her father lifted the chest Severn could not move. Grunting and puffing, they carried it down into the cabin and found a place for it.

"Mother must have packed stones in that one!" William laughed as he set it down.

"At least the effort warmed us," his father said.

Many things were still piled about. Severn was fitting bundles between chests stacked along one wall. He made everything fit.

"We stuff them in tight," he said to his sister. "Then we rope them together. That will keep them from bouncing when we hit the Skillet and Shoals. Otherwise we'd lose everything."

The perils of the journey seemed very close as she watched Severn loop the rope around the chests. She shivered.

William noticed her solemn face. He said, "Let's see, Father, I think we could fit Rachel in just about here. She'll fit tight."

He picked her up and thrust her into a narrow place between two husk mattresses. "That should take care of her. Give me a rope, Severn. I'll tie her in good and tight!"

"William!" she cried, struggling. "Let me go! Let me go this instant!"

"Oh, we must be sure you don't rattle about." William pretended to be very serious. "We must take good care of such a treasure."

"Perhaps we'd best pack her in a chest," Severn suggested. "We could feed her through a hole. At least I think we could."

"William!" Rachel protested, though she was giggling. "Let me go!"

Colonel Donelson smiled. "Come, boys. Our dinner is waiting for us. We'll consider how best to pack your sister as we walk home."

Two nights later the Donelsons were sitting around the fireplace in their cabin in the camp when they heard a loud knock.

Colonel Donelson went to the door and opened it. In stepped an old man with a fiddle under his arm. With him were two other men. Rachel knew one was Mr. Reuben Harrison.

"We've come to give you a treat!" he said. "This is my son. And this is my friend, Jonathan Pike, who will play for you."

Rachel clapped her hands. She had seen the old man around the camp, and had heard him play. It would be jolly to have some music. Rachel loved to sing. William had a fine voice, too, and Jane had a sweet one.

The Donelsons quickly made places around the hearth for the three newcomers.

"How kind of you!" Mrs. Donelson said. "I haven't heard music for months."

"You'll hear some now, madam," Mr. Pike said with a merry wink. "First, I'll play an Irish jig." He chuckled. "If we can't warm our feet, we can at least warm our hearts."

He sat on the edge of his chair, and tucked the fiddle under his chin. Everybody leaned for-forward to listen. How good it was to hear music after so much hard work.

Oh, how gay his music was! Rachel and Jane smiled at each other. Rachel began to tap one foot. What a pity the cabin was so small! How she'd like to dance a jig right now!

When Mr. Pike finished they all clapped.

"Come now," he said. "Surely some of you can carry a tune. What shall it be?"

" 'Lord Randall,' " Jane suggested.

" 'Lord Randall' it shall be!" cried Mr. Pike. He began to play the old ballad, and Jane started to sing:

"O where hae you been, Lord Randall, my son?
O where hae you been, my handsome young
man? . . ."

It went through many verses. At the end Rachel said, "I feel so sorry when young Lord Randall dies. It's a sad song. Let's sing a gay one."

"What would you like, my dear?" Mr. Pike asked. "How about this?"

"Oh, I know the words to that tune," Rachel said with delight. "It's a funny song!" She began the first verse:

"Fox went out on a chilly night,
Prayed for the moon to give him light . . ."

Soon everyone was singing with her. Mr. Pike ended the song with a flourish of his bow. Everyone clapped loudly. Rachel thought happily, "This is the most fun we've had here."

Then Mr. Pike put his fiddle down and the men began to talk seriously about the journey. "I figure we'll be ready to start in about ten days," Colonel Donelson said.

As they talked on, Rachel grew drowsy. She leaned against her mother and fell fast asleep. She was dreaming of the voyage when Mrs. Donelson shook her gently.

"Wake up, child. It's late and the gentlemen are leaving. Time for bed."

The Great Voyage

On December 22, 1779, at Camp Patrick Henry there was great excitement. In spite of bitter-cold weather, the flatboats had been finished. All the Donelsons' goods were aboard the "Adventure." The river party was ready to start.

Men pushed each boat away from the bank with poles, then jumped aboard. The very first one off was the "Adventure."

"We're moving!" Rachel cried. The big boat headed slowly out into the sluggish, icy river. "We're on our way!"

"Hurrah for the Great French Salt Lick!" yelled Sam and William.

It was hard, though, to hear what they said. Their lips were stiff with cold.

He and Rachel wanted to watch the other boats cast off, but the sharp wind made their faces burn and brought tears to their eyes.

"Let's go inside," Rachel suggested.

In the little cabin a bright fire burned on the hearth. Aunt Callie already had a pot of stew cooking. Corn pones were mixed and shaped, ready to bake on the Dutch oven before the fire. It seemed very homelike.

Rachel sniffed. The stew smelled wonderful. "I'm going to like traveling!"

Here by the fire Sam forgot about the cold outside. "I bet we have some real adventures!"

A few days later Rachel did not think a journey so fine. The cabin was so crowded! Often it was smoky and always it was very dark. There was hardly room to cook, eat, and sleep. The children were accustomed to running about.

Rachel grew bored. She had no real work to do. There was no space to play. She and Leven soon got tired of riddles and guessing games. Before long they knew all the answers. They could think of nothing new.

Sometimes Sam was called to help the men on deck. If the boat got stuck in the ice or on rocks under shallow water, they had to push it along with poles. Often this meant long hours of work in the bitter wind.

Nearly every day her father took out a book and wrote something in it. Rachel was curious.

"Father," she asked finally, "are you writing a story or a letter to somebody?"

"No, child, I'm keeping a journal of our trip. Each day I make a note of the things that happened. It's a remarkable undertaking—such a large fleet of flatboats traveling on this river. Later travelers may be glad to know what happened to us, and so I'm recording it."

"I wish I could keep a journal—or do anything except sit by the fire," Rachel said restlessly. "I'd like to do something."

Her mother opened a chest and took out some hanks of wool and knitting needles.

"You can sew well, Rachel. You can spin and weave a little. I don't know why I never taught you to knit. Now is certainly the time for it. The men need more wool stockings. When their feet get wet their stockings freeze. It's hard to get anything dry in this weather. All of the men are suffering from chilblains."

"Oh, Mother, I'd love to know how to knit! Poor Sam didn't have any dry stockings to put on yesterday. Let me make some for him first, and then I'll make extra pairs for all the others. Teach me now."

In the dim light it was hard to learn how to "turn" the stockings at the heel. But knitting helped to pass the long hours.

The fleet had moved slowly at first. Then, for nearly two months, low water and ice stopped the boats. A storm would have to raise the level of the river before they could cross the shoals. Everyone hoped for rain, but instead the weather turned even colder.

One afternoon when the boats were icebound Mrs. Donelson asked women from other boats to come to the "Adventure" and knit in its warm cabin. Mrs. Reuben Harrison praised the stockings Rachel had made.

"I want to knit a fine pair for Father," Rachel told her. "Better than these I've made for Sam. I'll try even harder on my next ones."

The women enjoyed working together and exchanging news.

"Our boat was scraped by rocks," Mrs. Robertson said. "It took hours to repair it. I wish I'd traveled by land with my husband. We never dreamed the river trip would be so hard."

"The voyage is taking so much longer than we expected," Mrs. Donelson agreed. "I'm afraid we shall all run out of food. The smaller boats couldn't carry much."

"On almost every boat someone is sick or injured," added another woman.

"This weather is hard on all of us," said Mrs. Harrison, "but it's dreadful for the poor people in the smaller boats. Did you know old Jonathan Pike is very sick?"

"The fiddler?" Rachel asked. "Why, he's our friend. We must bring him medicine and food. He's given us so much pleasure by playing the fiddle for us."

"He hasn't enough food—or enough shelter in his dugout. He's feverish and his cough is getting worse. I'm worried about him."

Rachel looked alarmed. "Oh, Mother, can't we help him? Can't we take him something to eat? We can see what else he needs."

"Tomorrow," Mrs. Donelson said, "Rachel and I will see what we can do for the sick people in the party."

The next morning she got out her chest of medicine and brewed some herb tea. Aunt Callie made a big kettle of soup.

"Mother, I can go with you, can't I?" Rachel was eager to get off the "Adventure" for a while, and she did want to see the old fiddler.

"I'll be glad to have your help. The soup is done now. Somerset can carry it."

Mrs. Donelson put on her cloak and picked up a small chest of medicine. She gave a smaller box to Rachel. "Wrap yourself up warmly, child. You don't know how sharp it is outside. You've been close to a fire for days."

They climbed up to the deck. Whooooooo! How cold the wind was! Rachel tried to shield her face with her cloak. But she could not hold the box with one hand.

The wind blew her cloak back. She would just have to stand it. Soon her face and her hands and feet ached with the cold. This was worse than Fort Henry.

Everywhere she saw men at work around the boats. Some carried wood from the shore. Some were tightening ropes. Some were mending jagged holes in planks torn by rocks.

Deep snow covered the riverbank where the fleet was tied up. Somerset waded easily through it, but Rachel and her mother slipped and slid. Soon they were shivering and their eyes watered from the cold.

They went from boat to boat and visited each sick person in the party.

Rachel admired her mother. Mrs. Donelson seemed to know just what to do for each illness or injury. Her visit cheered the people, and so did the soup she ladled out and reheated for the invalids on each boat.

"Why haven't any of these people thought to make soup?" Rachel asked through chattering teeth. She and her mother were struggling through the drifts near the end of the row of boats. "Don't they know it's good for people who are ill? They can make soup."

"Because their food is getting so low. Hoe-cake and dried venison are about all they have, anyway. They are suffering from hunger." There was worry in her mother's voice.

"Is our food giving out too?" Rachel asked.

"The meat is. I put our last fresh meat into that soup. I hope the men can bring us more soon. John went hunting in the woods yesterday, but he said the snow was deep and the animals were scarce. He's trying to trap rabbits today."

"Can't we have mush or pone bread?"

"Yes—but if we don't have any meat our supply of meal may give out before we reach the French Salt Lick."

She looked so grave that Rachel asked in a frightened voice, "What will we do?"

Mrs. Donelson glanced down at her daughter's anxious face, which was almost blue with cold. She smiled bravely. "The good Lord will provide. He always has. Perhaps farther down the river it will be warmer."

Rachel felt that there was nothing her mother could not endure. She straightened her own shoulders. She would try to be just as brave.

The last boat was a dugout, with a buffalo skin stretched over it. It formed a dark, cold tent. At one end a feeble fire burned in an iron pot.

There they found Jonathan Pike. He lay on a bale of household goods, wrapped in a thin, worn deerskin. His teeth chattered when he tried to speak. The dugout was almost as cold as the weather outside the boat.

Rachel's eyes filled with tears. She could not bear to see the kind old man so ill.

"We must build up your fire at once," Mrs. Donelson said briskly. "And you must keep your feet close to it. I'll give you some herb tea. It tastes bitter but it will cut down the fever."

Old Mr. Pike nodded feebly. Mrs. Donelson asked Somerset to get some wood and rebuild the fire. First he moved Mr. Pike's possessions about to make a better shelter.

"Put some soup in a bowl," Mrs. Donelson said to Rachel, "and feed it to our friend slowly. I'll find the medicines I need. When he has eaten I'll try to help that cough."

Feeding the old man wasn't easy, Rachel found. He was so weak he could hardly swallow. He coughed and spilled the soup. There was no space to move about in the little buffalo-hide tent. Rachel was tired and cold.

At last the bowl was empty. Mr. Pike looked stronger. He thanked her in a husky voice. Rachel was glad she had fed him.

Mrs. Donelson rubbed his chest well with mutton tallow. When she had finished she shook her head. Rachel wondered why. Was old Mr. Pike going to die?

"I'll leave some honey for your cough," Mrs. Donelson said. "Take a spoonful now and then."

His face brightened. Honey was a treat as well as good medicine.

As they started back to the "Adventure" Rachel asked in a low tone, "Mother, why did you shake your head?"

"He hasn't enough cover. I'm afraid he will get worse. I must have Somerset and the boys see that his fire is kept up."

Rachel stopped and set her box down. Before her mother noticed, she had turned and floundered back through the snow toward the dugout. As she went she untied the heavy brown cloak she wore. She was young and strong. She could stand the cold.

When she joined her mother again the cloak was gone. Mrs. Donelson guessed what Rachel had done. Tears came to her eyes. She stooped and kissed Rachel. "You're a good, generous girl. I'm proud of you."

Now Rachel felt that she could skim over the snow. It was good to think of old Jonathan Pike being warm and comfortable. He had smiled up at her when she tucked her cloak around him. The next day he was much better.

"I can't say enough to thank you," he told Mrs. Donelson. He held Rachel's hand. His fingers trembled but his voice was strong again. "You have fine boys. They came all through the night and kept up my fire. And this little girl—" he looked up at Rachel— "she gave me her own cloak. I'll never forget that. It kept me warm and now I think I'll get well."

He smiled at Rachel. "I hope to play for your dancing feet again!"

Attacked by Indians

AT last, in February, came a thaw, and then rainy days. The river began to rise. On February 28, 1780, Colonel Donelson wrote in his journal that the boats could now float over the shoals. The voyage began again.

Rachel thought she would always remember the sound of the rain. It came down in sheets. The river was rough and tossed the boats about.

Two days later Rachel was trying to help Leven learn to read. In the poor light they could hardly see the page of the primer. Suddenly Sam tumbled down the ladder into the cabin. "One of the boats is sinking!" he shouted.

His mother caught up her big shawl and hurried up to the deck. Leven and Rachel grabbed their wraps and followed.

The March wind was terrific. The river was choppy; the "Adventure" bobbed up and down so that they could hardly stand. All the boats were trying to pull close to an island. A flatboat had foundered on its rocky shore.

Near it the crew from the sinking boat splashed about in the water. Chests and boxes from its cargo floated around. The men were trying to save their belongings. Safe on the shore, the women and children watched anxiously. There seemed to be very little chance of saving the boat.

All day the men of the fleet worked to pull the boat away from the island, to the riverbank. They built a big fire there, and the poor shivering fellows would come out of the water and try to warm themselves by it.

The women kept hot porridge ready for them. Rachel helped bring the bowls of hot food from the "Adventure."

A great shout went up when at last the boat was pulled ashore. Now they could bail it out. Some of the cargo was saved. But most of the food was lost.

"We'll certainly have to be careful of our food," Rachel told her brothers that night.

"Young Reuben Harrison went hunting on shore today. He hoped he could get some game," Sam said. "He hasn't come back yet. He must have gone a long way. Probably the animals are all hiding in their dens. Or they've gone where it's warmer. Everything here is frozen so solid there's nothing for them to eat."

"If only the river doesn't freeze again!" said Rachel. "I'm so anxious to get to the Lick!"

"Me too," Leven said. "I'm tired of this old boat. I want to sleep in a bed again."

That night Rachel was awakened by gunshots. She jumped up in fright from her pallet on the floor. "Is it Indians, Mother?"

"No, they're shooting to show Reuben Harrison where we are. Even if he is far away, he should hear the shots."

"How dreadful to be lost in the woods in the cold and dark!" Rachel shivered. She could not go back to sleep for a long time.

Reuben had not returned the next morning. The men fired a small cannon, hoping he would hear that. All day and night they waited. They fired the cannon or muskets every hour. But the young man did not come back.

"Poor Mrs. Harrison!" Mrs. Donelson said, after she visited the grief-stricken woman. "I couldn't give her much comfort."

The whole party rejoiced when Reuben was found. He had made his way out of the woods and was waiting on the shore.

The boats moved slowly on down the Tennessee River. One day in March Rachel went up to the deck. The wind was nipping, but not so icy now. Along the shore she could see the first green shoots and buds. Perhaps the winter would end soon. How she longed for spring.

It was good to be out in the open air again. Rachel ran lightly from one side of the boat to the other. Then she watched her father and William. They were using long, stout poles to keep the craft away from boulders by the shore.

"Let me try that! I've sat still so many months. I want to use my muscles."

Her brother smiled, but shook his head. "This takes too much strength. Feel how the current strikes the pole."

Rachel grasped the pole below his hands. She looked up in surprise. "I guess you're right. I'd better not try. The water tugs at it so hard. I probably couldn't hold on."

As she moved away, she cried, "Look, Father! There are Indians on the other bank, See?"

He gazed across the river. A number of red men were getting into canoes. "I hope they're friendly!" he said.

He called to all the men on the "Adventure." All of them got their guns out.

Rachel stared at the Indians fearfully. Would they scalp her whole family? But as they drew nearer she said, "Why, they are friendly! See, they're waving. One is smiling."

The Indians paddled right up to the "Adventure." Several raised their hands in greeting and shouted, "Brothers!" They appeared to be very friendly. Rachel was relieved.

The Donelson men held their guns ready but did not object when the Indians in the first canoe asked to climb aboard. The smiling one did the talking. He said his name was Archy Coody. He was a half-breed.

The other braves had once lived on the Chickamauga town on the south bank. They wanted to tell the colonel that the current there was better for flatboats. There were hidden rocks close to the surface on the north bank.

Rachel kept as quiet as a mouse. She hoped Father would not send her inside. It was exciting to be so close to Indians. They looked savage, with red and black paint on their faces. But they seemed nice. When Archy Coody smiled at her, she bobbed her head. She wondered if she should curtsy. She wanted to be just as courteous and polite as she could be.

Then she noticed that the river was full of canoes. While Coody talked, many Indians had paddled toward the fleet. The half-breed and his braves left the "Adventure," still smiling. But a few moments later the Indians opened fire on the fleet. The friends had turned into a war party!

Quickly Rachel crouched down behind a barrel. She trembled with anger more than fear. How she wished she had a gun! The Indians didn't know she was there. She'd especially like to shoot that treacherous Coody for pretending to be friendly to the settlers.

The fast current soon carried the first boats past the old Indian town. The "Adventure" was out of danger, but in the distance Rachel could hear shooting, and then screams and pitiful cries. Would the Indians follow them?

When she came out from her hiding place her father said, "Rachel! Child, I'd forgotten you were on deck. Get inside quickly, and tell your mother John and I must go back to find out what happened to the other boats. I fear that Mr. Stuart's family has suffered. His boat was alone, far behind the others, because his children have smallpox. I heard their cries."

Colonel Donelson and the boys all looked grim. He and John got in the canoe that floated behind the "Adventure," and picked up their paddles. Before they had gone very far, other settlers in their own canoes joined the Donelsons. All of these men paddled as fast as they could to the Stuart flatboat.

"Oh, Father, be careful," Rachel cried before she hurried down to the cabin.

Mrs. Donelson was at the door. Jane and Aunt Callie huddled together in one corner, Leven peeked out from behind their skirts.

She poured out her story and gave her father's message. "Oh, Mother!" she added. "Those Indians pretended to be friends."

"Thank God no one on the 'Adventure' was wounded! We have every reason to be thankful that none of us were harmed."

"But, Mother, I thought all the Indians had been driven away from the river towns."

"Your father says the British must have given them supplies so that they could resettle in the towns Colonel Shelby destroyed."

"I'll be glad when we are past those towns," Rachel said. "The Indians may be waiting for us at any point. They must know by this time that we are coming."

"All of us will be glad when we have passed them," Jane agreed. "Oh, Rachel, I was so frightened for you!"

"I'd have shot those bad old Indians if I'd had a gun! *Pow! Pow!*" Leven shouted, jumping about. "I'd have shot all of them!"

"So would I!" Then Rachel remembered the strange, painted faces. "But I was glad to find a hiding place, too."

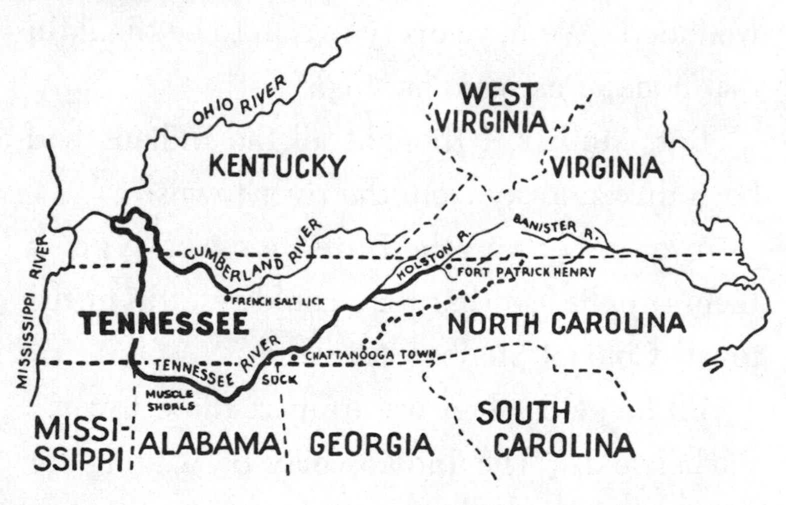

The heavy line traces Rachel's journey on the flatboat.

Rachel to the Rescue!

THE boats did not all pass the Indian towns safely. Several families were wiped out. As Colonel Donelson feared, everyone on the Stuart boat was killed. The Indians hated the white settlers who were coming to their lands. They killed any who had to stop to repair their boats.

While the river party was still grieving over friends, the boats reached the place called the Suck. The mountains forced the river into a deep, narrow channel here. The water rushed through, swirling in a terrifying way. It threatened to dash the boats against the high bluffs on either side.

Jane and Rachel could not bear to stay in the cabin. The roar of the water was deafening.

"I'd rather be washed off the boat than squashed in here," Jane said.

"Me too," said Rachel. "Let's go outside."

Water was splashing over the deck of the "Adventure." Rachel clung to her sister.

"We're going so fast!"

"We'll never get through!" Jane shrieked.

Suddenly they felt the strong current pull the boat sideways. They saw Rafe, a Negro servant who was helping to pole it away from the bluffs, fall. His pole had struck a rock under the surface. The blow had knocked him down.

"We'll sink!" Jane staggered to the cabin and clung to the doorway.

Rachel dropped down. On her hands and knees she crawled toward the man. He had struck his head on a box. In vain he tried to get to his feet.

"Hold onto the pole, Rafe!" she cried. I'm coming! I'll help you!"

Could she really take the pole? She remembered how the water had tugged at the one William held. And here it was so much rougher! But she *must* try.

In the noise of the Suck it was useless to call for help. Severn was not far away but she could never make him hear. Her father and William were clear across the deck.

The "Adventure" tossed and jerked. Rachel's fingers slipped on the wet deck. Suppose she were washed off into that terrible whirlpool! But she kept going. At last she reached the pole. Rafe still clutched it with one hand.

Rachel grasped it firmly. Then she had to get to her feet. Next she had to get to the stanchion at the edge of the deck! The stanchion was a low post, and the rope with which they tied up the boat at night was made fast to it.

If she could reach it, she could brace herself against it. Rachel crawled along the deck until she could grip the pole. With one hand she pulled herself up. It had taken only a few seconds, but it seemed an hour. She thrust the pole out toward the bluffs. The boat steadied.

"If I can just keep pushing against the rocks," she thought, "the boat won't hit them."

The boat barely missed one of the large rocks that stuck out of the water. Rachel knew that if the "Adventure" struck one it would founder and sink. She pushed harder.

There was another, just ahead! She leaned against the stanchion and shoved hard with the pole. The "Adventure" slipped past the rock. It went sailing by, safe!

Rachel felt as if she might faint, she was so relieved. Then a pair of strong hands covered her own. She looked up. There was John, his face white. Suddenly she was exhausted.

"Brave girl!" he yelled in her ear. "I'll take it. Be careful. And go back in the cabin!"

As she reached the door Rachel heard a cry. She looked about and saw that a small boat following them had turned turtle.

Jane hurried out to pull Rachel into the cabin. "You must get warm and dry. You're drenched, and you're trembling."

When they heard shots outside, Rachel wanted to go back, but her mother stopped her. "What have you been doing?" she asked sternly.

Jane spoke up. "She saved the 'Adventure'! She guided the boat when old Rafe fell. She kept us off the rocks." Jane was so wrought up she was almost weeping.

Just then the boat seemed to settle down quietly. The fearsome sound of rushing water was heard no more. They were safely through the Suck. They could relax, at least for a little while, Rachel thought wearily.

An hour later William and Severn came in. Both boys looked excited.

"They know how I saved the boat," Rachel thought. She felt proud and happy.

But Severn said. "Did you hear the shots? There were Indians up on the bluffs!"

"They tried to kill the people from the boat that turned over," William said angrily. "But the Suck saved us after all. We were moving too fast for them!"

"Was anyone hurt?" asked Mrs. Donelson.

"Four wounded, but none badly. And, Mother, there's a brave girl on one of these boats. We are all proud of her."

"Now William will tell about me." Rachel smiled to herself.

"On the Gower boat—their daughter Nancy. She's just a little older than Rachel. She was helping to pole and one of those so-called 'braves' shot her. But she didn't give up."

"Tell us what happened," Jane said.

"She stayed at her post until we were out of the Suck. Then her mother saw that Nancy had been shot by the Indians."

"Mrs. Gower wants to know if you have any bandages, Mother," Severn added. "I'll take them to her. The boats are pulling in to the bank, to take care of the wounded."

Mrs. Donelson got out lint and linen for the bandages. Rachel sat very still. She was glad she had been able to help. But she almost wished she had been shot—once, anyway—so that her brothers would brag about her.

"And if only I could have brought the boat all the way through the Suck!" she thought. "Then they'd say I stayed at my post and didn't give up." She felt like crying. It had been hard to hold the pole. Her hands were bruised and cut and full of splinters. But nobody had noticed, because she hadn't been wounded.

Just then John came in. "Did you hear about Nancy Gower, Mother?"

"Yes, She's a brave girl. I'm sending some bandages and salve for her."

"We have a brave girl on the 'Adventure,' too." John put his arm around Rachel. "She took over when Rafe was knocked down. She handled his pole like a man!"

"I'm very proud of her." Her mother smiled at Rachel. That was the reward Rachel had longed for.

The expedition came at last to the famous Muscle Shoals. Before they tried to run through them, all the boats pulled in to the shore. The men shifted the cargo of each to distribute the weight evenly.

Water rushing rapidly over the rocks made an uproar louder than that of the Suck. On the islands were big piles of driftwood, cast there by currents running in all directions.

Sam said in a gloomy voice, "Father heard the Shoals are about twenty-five miles long."

A few months earlier Rachel would have felt panic. But she had seen plenty of danger now. She felt more confident. She answered quietly, "I hope we can get through."

"We must pray for God's deliverance," Colonel Donelson said. They all knelt on the deck. Rachel could scarcely hear her father's words over the roar of wind and water.

Everyone was very serious when the boats entered the Shoals. For three hours they were knocked about. The men had to struggle desperately to save their craft. Sometimes they dragged on the rough, rocky bottom. All feared they would be wrecked. But at last they were safely through.

Behind them the roar of the Shoals grew fainter. "My ears feel funny!" Rachel exclaimed. "It seems so quiet now."

That night as usual Colonel Donelson took out his journal. Rachel leaned against his shoulder. The dim light from a tallow candle shone on their faces.

He wrote slowly and carefully. The goose-quill pen made a soft scratching.

Rachel read the words as he wrote: . . . "by the hand of Providence, we are now preserved from this danger also."

The wind was still very cold. But there was a smell of spring in the air. Birds were coming back. One March day Rachel heard a wren singing. "Oh, Sam! Listen! A wren. Wrens are my favorite birds."

"I thought wood thrushes were." Sam was sitting on the deck, cleaning his gun.

"I do love them." Rachel shook back her dark curls. "But they're sad. The wren is always cheerful. Remember what Mother used to tell us Jenny Wren says?"

" 'Be cheerful! Be cheerful! Be sweeeeet!' I could be more cheerful," he added, "if only I had enough to eat again. Think of the good food we used to have every day in Virginia."

Now the waters were peaceful, but the supply of food was so low that everybody was always hungry. The famished men could hardly find the strength to manage the boats.

"Oh, Sam! Wouldn't roast chicken taste wonderful? And a bed would feel heavenly! I'm sick and tired of this old boat! I pray every night that we reach the Lick soon. I want to live in a house and have a garden again."

"What! Have you had enough adventure? Are you tired of journeying?"

"Yes," said Rachel, "I've had enough excitement to last me for a lifetime."

"I'd even eat Old Gobbler if you had brought him," Sam teased.

"Mother said he'd be as hard as flint."

"I wouldn't care. I just hope there is some food stored at the Lick," Sam said. "All I can think about is eating!"

There was no corn meal left. They could not even make bread.

The travelers were living on greens. Whenever the boats were tied up the women and children looked along the shore for dandelions, pokeweed, or lamb's-lettuce. They called this Shawnee salad because they knew the Indians ate it. But they needed meat.

The men hunted for game, but they seldom found any. The long, cold winter had killed or starved out almost all the animals.

Along the Cumberland River, finally, the men killed some buffaloes. They dug a big pit and built a fire in it. The women roasted the meat.

"I can't wait till it's cooked!" Sam said.

Rachel answered, "I'm so hungry I can . . . I can . . . well, I can feel it in my teeth!"

Sam shouted with laughter. He knew what his sister meant. It would be good to set one's teeth into something.

When the meat was done, it tasted delicious. It was almost like having a picnic. Everybody ate his fill. Even Sam had enough. And there was more left, to take with them.

Up the Cumberland River the boats went. Rachel knew that this was the final stage of the journey. But it seemed to go on and on.

"The last miles always seem the longest," said her mother, "especially if you want very much to reach the end of a trip."

On April twenty-fourth, four long months after they had left Camp Patrick Henry, the weary, hungry travelers came to the end of their voyage. They had floated nearly a thousand miles. Thirty-three persons had been lost or drowned or captured by Indians or had died of cold or illness. Indians had wounded nine.

What a joy it was to see cabins! And to see their friends again! The men whom Captain Robertson had led over the Wilderness Trail were all there. What a happy reunion!

"The new-plowed fields look wonderful to me," Colonel Donelson said. "Though it's late in April, the warm sun will soon bring up the seeds we'll plant."

"I'm going to plant my daffodil bulbs, too," Rachel said. "I hope I never have to move them. I'll never wish for a journey or adventure again!"

Mistress of the Hermitage

THE Donelsons soon had a new home by the Cumberland River, near the Great French Salt Lick. The name which had sounded strange to Rachel was changed to Fort Nash. But it was still a rough little frontier settlement. Later it became Nashboro, then Nashville. Slowly the settlement grew into a town, the capital of the state of Tennessee.

Meanwhile, Rachel grew into a beautiful young woman. Everyone admired her big dark eyes, her curly hair, her bright face and dimples. They said she was cheerful and generous, with high spirits and a kind heart.

The older Donelson children married and moved to homesteads of their own. They all lived close to the blockhouse their father had built. Rachel and her mother were glad, for they missed Colonel Donelson sadly. On a wilderness journey he had been killed by Indians.

One day in 1788 a tall, lanky young man knocked on the Widow Donelson's door. He had a long, thin face, bright blue eyes and a shock of red hair.

"Please, ma'am," he said, "my name is Andrew Jackson. A friend told me you take a few boarders. I wonder if you could rent me a room?"

He explained he was a lawyer from North Carolina. He wanted to open a law office in Nashville. He looked honest and polite, and Mrs. Donelson liked him. She let him share a cabin on her place with another young man. Since she and Rachel were alone, she welcomed the two gentlemen as a protection against Indians.

The moment he met Rachel, Andrew Jackson thought, "She's the prettiest woman I've ever seen. I intend to marry her—if she'll have me." He tried to think of ways to please Rachel and serve her. He helped Mrs. Donelson when her sons were away. He was always thoughtful, polite and gentle. For several years he showed Rachel how kind and loyal he could be, and how much he loved her.

So, when he begged her to marry him, Rachel said "Yes." For she had fallen in love with Andrew, too.

Life was not easy for the young couple at first. Andrew Jackson had very little money, but he bought a small plantation, with a crude log house. They had one young servant girl, named Hannah, to help Rachel with the housework.

One day when Rachel showed Hannah how to perform some task she told the girl how she had learned it back in Virginia.

"Dear me, Hannah! How I used to dislike girls' work!" she exclaimed, laughing. "I wanted to play all day with my brothers. But now I'm very glad my mother made me learn how to be a housekeeper. I want to manage Mr. Jackson's house so he'll be proud of it."

Young Mrs. Jackson was a good neighbor, too. She could not bear to think anyone near her was needy, hungry or sick. Often she would say, "Help me pack a basket, Hannah. Mr. Jackson said a poor family up the road doesn't have enough food." Or she would say, "Hannah, I must ride down to the Elliotts' this morning. Their baby girl is sick. Maybe I can help."

Then she would mount her horse and Hannah would hand up the basket of food or medicine. And Rachel would ride away, as her mother had done, to aid and comfort a neighbor.

Rachel was happy. She was proud of her husband and of their new place.

Young Lawyer Jackson was lucky. He was ambitious, and he worked hard. More and more clients came to him. Soon he could afford to give Rachel a small coach. He bought a larger, better plantation, called Hunter's Hill.

Rachel wished only that Andrew never had to be away on business.

She talked of this one summer day as they walked up to a knoll on their plantation. Rachel gazed out over the rolling fields of the Cumberland Valley. "It's so beautiful!" she sighed. "And I'm so happy. I always am, when you are here. I love this valley. I love my home."

Andrew reached over and took her hand. "But it's not good enough for you, dearest. I'm going to give you a much finer house and more servants someday. You're going to have everything a woman could possibly want. I mean to surround you with happiness. Whatever my Rachel wants is my own dearest wish."

Rachel smiled at him lovingly. She would rather live very simply. But she knew how happy it made Andrew to give her fine presents and to plan a splendid future for them both.

Andrew kept his promise. He worked hard at his law practice. Whatever Rachel mentioned, Andrew ordered. He bought her pretty china, handsome sofas, chairs and beds. He bought her lovely satin gowns. He also spent a great deal of money buying land.

At last he had to tell Rachel he was in debt. He would have to sell Hunter's Hill. They could move to a plantation called the Hermitage. It had only a big old blockhouse, with a stockade around it. It was very simple and bare.

He looked so unhappy Rachel tried to cheer him. "I'll like that. I lived in a blockhouse for years. I don't care about a grand home. And it will be so nice to be near Nashville. All the Donelsons live closer to the Hermitage."

Andrew was stubborn. "Someday," he declared, "the Hermitage will be the beautiful house I want for you."

"I like it now," Rachel said gaily. "Just think, all of my nieces and nephews can visit us easily! I can borrow any of the Donelson babies. There'll be plenty of room for them to play. I'm glad we're going to live there."

Andrew and Rachel had no children. Because she was lonely when he was away, Rachel invited several nephews and nieces to live with her. She and Andrew brought them up, sent them to school and loved them as their own. They even adopted one of Severn's sons, and named him Andrew Jackson, Jr.

All the children in the neighborhood loved to visit the Hermitage. Aunt Rachel spoiled them and played with them. She could tell thrilling stories of Indians and of the voyage of the "Adventure."

Finally Andrew could afford to rebuild the Hermitage. Then it truly became the beautiful home he had always planned for Rachel.

She would rather have had Andrew himself. But he was now a soldier. The young United States was now in the War of 1812, and he went south to fight, first as a captain, then as a general. He defeated the Creek Indians in Alabama. He won a great victory over the British in the battle of New Orleans. Then he pushed east to capture the Spanish town of Pensacola.

Rachel managed the plantation while he was away. She tried to keep so busy she would not worry about him. She was very glad to have the Donelson children with her.

One day she called them to the parlor. There, beside her, stood a little boy about young Andy's size. Rachel was smiling. "This is your new brother," she announced. The boy stared gravely at the children. He had big black eyes.

"Why, Aunt Rachel," said young John Donelson, "isn't he an Indian?"

Rachel nodded. "He is a little Creek Indian boy who needs a home. His name is Lincoyer. I want you all to be kind to him. He has had a hard time, and he needs kindness and love."

The children were curious. "Where did he come from? Where did you find him?"

"Your Uncle Andrew has sent him to us. Lincoyer was captured in a battle in Alabama. His own people refused to take care of him. The General says Lincoyer made him think of Andy."

Andy walked up to the Indian boy. "I'll be his brother," he said. "I'll love him, too. I'll—I'll give him something nice."

Little Emily Donelson, who was spending the day, ran over too. "I will love him, Aunt Rachel." She took Lincoyer's hand. He did not smile, but he did not pull away. He just stared at her. The other children crowded around.

Rachel smiled. "The General says Lincoyer likes brown sugar."

"Let's get some from the kitchen," Emily cried. "Let's get it right now!"

The children rushed out, taking the Indian boy with them. Soon Rachel heard them outside, laughing together. Even little Lincoyer was shouting with laughter. Suddenly she felt very happy. Lincoyer had a home. And she had another child.

After the war General Andrew Jackson came back to Tennessee a hero. Rachel was prouder of him than ever. She was pleased when he told her how well she had managed the plantation. Now surely the General would stay at home!

General Jackson had hoped to spend the rest of his life at the Hermitage with Rachel. Every day, however, he was receiving letters from all parts of the Union, asking him to be a candidate for President of the United States. "Old

Hickory," as he was called, had never sought a public office. But he would not shrink from a public responsibility.

At last, he told Rachel, she would have the kind of honors he had always wanted to give her. In Washington she would be the First Lady of the Land, mistress of the White House.

She did not tell Andrew that she might not live to see him made President. He did not know how ill she had been for several years.

Shortly before they were to leave Tennessee she died quietly in the beautiful home Andrew had made for her. The General was heartbroken. The Presidency meant little to him now.

The day before he went to Washington he sat down at his desk at the Hermitage. He wanted to write an epitaph for Rachel. He was a rough, hard-bitten old soldier who usually had little to say. What could he write now, to express his devotion to Rachel?

He thought about the years they had spent together. A tender look came over his thin, lined, weather-beaten face. He began to write:

Her face was fair, her person pleasing, her temper amiable, her heart kind. She delighted in relieving the wants of her fellow creatures. . . . To the poor she was a benefactor, to the rich an example, to the wretched a comforter, to the prosperous an ornament. . . .

The beautiful Hermitage still stands, just north of Nashville, Tennessee. Every year thousands of visitors go to see it. They walk through the rooms that Andrew and Rachel planned. They see her portrait hanging on the wall. They can walk up the wide, curving stairs and stand on the balcony that overlooks her garden.

Rachel and Andrew seem to live forever in the peace and graciousness of the Hermitage.

More About This Book

WHEN RACHEL JACKSON LIVED

1767 RACHEL DONELSON WAS BORN IN ACCOMAC COUNTY, VIRGINIA, JUNE 15.

The Thirteen Colonies were governed by Great Britain.

The estimated population of the colonies was about 2,210,000.

1767–1791 RACHEL GREW UP ON PLANTATIONS IN VIRGINIA AND TENNESSEE.

The Revolutionary War was fought with England, 1775-1783.

The Declaration of Independence was signed, 1776.

The Constitutional Convention met, 1787.

George Washington became first President, 1789.

1791–1804 RACHEL DONELSON MARRIED ANDREW JACKSON AND CONTINUED TO LIVE IN TENNESSEE.

Eli Whitney invented the cotton gin, 1793.

Tennessee became the sixteenth state, 1796.

Andrew Jackson was elected to the U.S. House of Representatives, 1796.

Andrew Jackson was elected a justice of the state supreme court, 1797.

The United States bought the Louisiana Territory from France, 1803.

1804–1822 RACHEL AND ANDREW JACKSON BEGAN TO LIVE AT THE HERMITAGE.

Lewis and Clark explored the Northwest, 1804-1806.

The War of 1812, in which Andrew Jackson was a general, was fought, 1812-1814.

Jackson defeated the Seminole Indians in Florida, 1818.

Florida was purchased from Spain, 1819.

1822–1828 RACHEL AND ANDREW JACKSON ENTERTAINED FAMOUS PEOPLE AT THE HERMITAGE.

Andrew Jackson was elected senator from Tennessee, 1823.

Andrew Jackson, the first candidate to be nominated for President by the Democratic Party, was elected, 1828.

1828 RACHEL JACKSON DIED AT THE HERMITAGE, DECEMBER 22.

There were twenty-four states in the Union.

John Quincy Adams was President.

The population of the country was about 12,865,000.

DO YOU REMEMBER?

1. What words and date did little Rachel sew on her sampler?
2. Who was Rachel's father, and why was he often away from home?
3. Who was Aunt Callie, and where did she live?
4. How did Rachel help her mother and brothers during an Indian raid?
5. How did Rachel help her father and Sam on their surveying trip?
6. How did Governor Patrick Henry come to get a piece of Rachel's first apple pie?
7. What preparations did the Donelsons make for their long trip to Tennessee?
8. Why did the settlers stay at Camp Patrick Henry for several weeks?

9. What hardships did they endure during their long journey on the rivers?
10. How did Rachel manage to save the "Adventure" during the attack by the Indians?
11. How did Rachel meet Andrew Jackson?
12. What was Andrew Jackson's occupation when he married Rachel?
13. What famous home near Nashville did Jackson and Rachel occupy?
14. Why did Rachel not get to accompany Jackson to Washington when he became President?
15. What fine things did Jackson write about Rachel in his epitaph?
16. Where may a large portrait of Rachel Jackson be seen today?

IT'S FUN TO LOOK UP THESE THINGS

1. Why did people use flatboats for moving wherever they could on the frontier?
2. Why did the people in Virginia think that Tennessee was a great distance away?
3. Why did the Indians cause more trouble in Tennessee than in Virginia?

4. Where is the Hermitage, and what may be seen there today?
5. What work did Rachel Jackson do while her husband was away at war?
6. What other presidents besides Andrew Jackson have come from Tennessee?
7. How many terms did Andrew Jackson serve as President?

INTERESTING THINGS YOU CAN DO

1. Draw a map to show the route which the Donelsons followed in moving westward from Virginia to Tennessee.
2. Find out what is located at Muscle Shoals today and give a report to the class.
3. Write a description of the Hermitage, where Rachel and Andrew Jackson lived.
4. Read about General Jackson's victory at New Orleans and tell why it was important.
5. Find out how Jackson traveled when he went to Washington from the Hermitage.
6. Write a story about the founding of the Democratic party which nominated Jackson.

OTHER BOOKS YOU MAY ENJOY READING

Andy Jackson: Boy Soldier, Augusta Stevenson. Trade and School Editions, Bobbs-Merrill.

Andy Jackson's Water Well, William O. Steele. Harcourt.

Her Christmas at the Hermitage, H. T. Miller. Longmans.

Jacksons of Tennessee, The, Marguerite Vance. Dutton.

Little House in the Big Woods, Laura Wilder. Harper.

Trails West and the Men Who Made Them, Edith Dorian and W. N. Wilson. Whittlesey.

INTERESTING WORDS IN THIS BOOK

candidate (kăn′dĭ dāt): person who seeks an elective office or is nominated for one

chilblain (chĭl′blān): sore on hands or feet caused by exposure to cold

current (kûr′ĕnt): flowing water, as in a stream

curtsy (kûrt′sĭ): special bow made by bending the knees

delicious (dė lĭsh′ŭs): pleasing to the taste

dugout (dŭg′out) : canoe or boat made by hollowing out a log

entertain (ĕn′tẽr tān′) : have as a guest

exhausted (ĕg zôst′ĕd) : tired out

expedition (ĕks′pē dĭsh′ŭn) : journey for a special purpose

flint (flĭnt) : hard kind of quartz which may be used for starting a fire

governor (gŭv′ẽr nẽr) : person holding the highest elective office in a state

hazard (hăz′ẽrd) : risk, danger

herb (ûrb) : seed plant used for making medicine or for seasoning food

hesitate (hĕz′ĭ tāt) : delay action because uncertain of what to do

militia (mĭ lĭsh ȧ) : body of citizens trained for military action but called into service only for emergency purposes

mutter (mŭt′ẽr) : talk in low, indistinct tones

oppression (ŏ prĕsh′ŭn) : cruel or unjust treatment

particular (pẽr tĭk′ū lẽr) : unusual, different from others

patriot (pā′trĭ ŭt) : person who loves and loyally supports his country

pewter (pū′tẽr) : mixture of copper and tin used in making tableware

plantation (plăn tā′shŭn) : large tract of land used for farming

porridge (pŏr′ĭj) : broth or soup made by mixing ground cereal in water or milk

poultice (pōl′tĭs) : thick substance, usually heated and spread on a cloth, used to reduce pain or inflammation in some part of the body

precious (prĕsh′ŭs) : costly, of great value

reassure (rē′ă shŏŏr′) : help to restore courage or confidence

sampler (sȧm′plẽr) : piece of needlework, showing letters or verses

skillet (skĭl′ĕt) : frying pan

smallpox (smôl′pŏks′) : contagious disease that usually leaves scars on the skin

strutted: walked proudly

treacherous (trĕch′ẽr ŭs) : dangerous, not to be trusted

varmints (vär′mĭnts) : small, obnoxious animals hard to control, same as vermin

venison (vĕn′ĭ z′n) : meat of a deer

Childhood
OF FAMOUS AMERICANS

JAMES OGLETHORPE, *Parks*
MYLES STANDISH, *Stevenson*
PETER STUYVESANT, *Widdemer*
POCAHONTAS, *Seymour*
SQUANTO, *Stevenson*
VIRGINIA DARE, *Stevenson*
WILLIAM BRADFORD, *Smith*
WILLIAM PENN, *Mason*

STRUGGLE for INDEPENDENCE

ANTHONY WAYNE, *Stevenson*
BEN FRANKLIN, *Stevenson*
BETSY ROSS, *Weil*
DAN MORGAN, *Bryant*
ETHAN ALLEN, *Winders*
FRANCIS MARION, *Steele*
GEORGE ROGERS CLARK, *Wilkie*
GEORGE WASHINGTON, *Stevenson*
ISRAEL PUTNAM, *Stevenson*
JOHN PAUL JONES, *Snow*
MARTHA WASHINGTON, *Wagoner*
MOLLY PITCHER, *Stevenson*
NATHAN HALE, *Stevenson*
NATHANAEL GREENE, *Peckham*
PATRICK HENRY, *Barton*
PAUL REVERE, *Stevenson*
TOM JEFFERSON, *Monsell*

ABIGAIL ADAMS, *[illegible]ner*
ALEC HAMILTON, *[illegible]gins*
ANDY JACKSON, *Stevenson*
DAN WEBSTER, *Smith*
DEWITT CLINTON, *Widdemer*
DOLLY MADISON, *Monsell*
ELIAS HOWE, *Corcoran*
ELI WHITNEY, *Snow*
FRANCIS SCOTT KEY, *Stevenson*
HENRY CLAY, *Monsell*
JAMES FENIMORE COOPER, *Winders*
JAMES MONROE, *Widdemer*
JOHN AUDUBON, *Mason*
JOHN JACOB ASTOR, *Anderson*
JOHN MARSHALL, *Monsell*
JOHN QUINCY ADAMS, *Weil*
LUCRETIA MOTT, *Burnett*
MATTHEW CALBRAITH PERRY, *Scharbach*
NANCY HANKS, *Stevenson*
NOAH WEBSTER, *Higgins*
OLIVER HAZARD PERRY, *Long*
RACHAEL JACKSON, *Govan*
ROBERT FULTON, *Henry*
SAMUEL MORSE, *Snow*
SEQUOYAH, *Snow*
STEPHEN DECATUR, *Smith*
STEPHEN FOSTER, *Higgins*
WASHINGTON IRVING, *Widdemer*
ZACK TAYLOR, *Wilkie*

WESTWARD MOVEMENT

BRIGHAM YOUNG, *Jordan and Frisbee*
BUFFALO BILL, *Stevenson*
DANIEL BOONE, *Stevenson*
DAVY CROCKETT, *Parks*
JED SMITH, *Burt*
JESSIE FREMONT, *Wagoner*
JIM BOWIE, *Winders*